D0988815

What the F***
Was That All About?

The Story of A Warrior's
Journey Home


By Tom Barber

Copyright © 2019 by A15 Publishing

All rights reserved. Published by A15 Publishing.

No part of this publication may be reproduced, distributed, or transmitted in any form or by any means, including photocopying, recording, or other electronic or mechanical methods, without the prior written permission of the publisher, except in the case of brief quotations embodied in critical reviews and certain other noncommercial uses permitted by copyright law. For permission requests, write to the publisher, addressed "Attention: Permissions Coordinator," at the address below or by e-mail at info@a15publishing.com

All illustrations done by the author and copyrighted.

A15 Publishing
PO Box 66054
Hampton, VA 23665
www.A15publishing.com

ISBN: 978-1-970155-01-3

FIRST PRINTING

Stories help satisfy our hunger for understanding
by allowing us to see ourselves in the lives of others.
They show us that this hunger is universal.
Stories show us we are not alone.

# Part I

# One

I woke up in a cold sweat.
Scared. Desperate. Hopeless. And losing ground fast.
*Would death be kind or come at me with more shit?*

Would Death Be Kind?

# Two

Sat up and swung my feet to the floor. Stared down at my shaking hands. Turned and ripped a fresh beer from the six-pack on the bed beside me. Chugged it down.

Then, in a flash of anger, I crushed the empty can in my fist and threw it across the room as hard as I could. With a crash and a rattle, it hit the wall and fell to the floor to join the others.

*Another dead soldier.*

Me? Deep inside: cold, hungry, and pissed off at the world.

My face in my hands, I groaned.

"Fuckin' war."

Been through too many nights like this.

*No more. No more…*

Cold, Hungry, and Pissed Off at the World

# Three

"Sit down, man. We gotta talk."

Anger flared again. My jaw muscles tightened.

*Who the hell does this guy think he is, giving me orders?*

I was a decent size, but this guy was big. Broad shoulders, piercing blue eyes, long hair and beard that was grey and grizzled.

My eyes swept the area. I made a move to swing wide.

Just not fast enough.

The guy took his foot off the desk and shoved a chair across the sidewalk with it. Timing was perfect. It chattered to a stop right in front of me.

Adrenaline pumped.

Had a backpack slung over my shoulder with a twelve-pack of beer in it. Hurl it at the guy? Looked down at the chair. Bigger package. Bent down and grabbed it, ready for the throw.

Decision time.

"Don't do it, soldier."

*Soldier? How the hell did he know?*

Busted, I froze. The look in the guy's eyes said the same thing: *Don't do it.*

Stalemate. Mexican standoff.

# Four

"I said sit down."

I didn't. Just stood there and stared back at the guy.

"You need help," he said. "Saw you comin' a mile away. I ain't in the jungle anymore, an' you sure as hell ain't in the desert, but that look is universal."

"The look?" I said with suspicion.

"Yeah. You know. Keyed up. Jittery. Head on a swivel. And the look in the eyes. Fierce. Haunted. Hopeless. The eyes of a man looking for a way out."

Busted again. I was headed wherever I needed to go to get into a fight and get myself killed, *and this guy knew it.*

"And besides," the guy said, "punchin' your own ticket as an easy way out might not work too well."

"What do you mean?" I said, still guarded.

"Might end up carryin' around the same shit with ya on the other side." He paused. "Who knows? Give it some thought."

"But on the other hand," he said, "I was once told that if you've never really thought about suicide, you haven't lived a full life. Ain't that the balls? If you've never really thought about takin' yourself out, you're incomplete? But here you are *lookin'* for a way to get yourself killed, so now you *are* complete. You're playin' with a full deck."

He spread his hands wide.

"Ya got it all."

*Got it all? What's with this guy? Here I am looking down the barrel and he's telling me I've got all my shit squared away?*

Forget it. My outer defenses were taking a beating here.

He must have seen me trying to hold it together and said, "Sorry, man. I always try a little humor in the beginnin'. See how it goes."

I just looked at him.

# Five

Then, with some serious effort, I pulled myself together and once more my eyes swept the area.

The guy was sitting in a pale green, overstuffed chair in the shade of an old storefront. I was standing in the sun, and it was hot.

He was alone. Wore faded jeans and a camo t-shirt. In front of him, the desk. Grey metal. Government issue. Daily newspaper spread across the surface. A pitcher of what looked like iced tea. Three glasses. One full. Two empty. Two grey metal chairs, also government issue, one of which stood defiantly in front of me.

A hand-painted sign on cardboard was stuck to the inside of the store window with duct tape.

*Mitchell's Place.*

The place looked a little rough around the edges. Of course, the hood was a rough one. Tough getting yourself killed in Mr. Roger's neighborhood.

Didn't seem to bother this guy, though. Looked pretty comfortable hanging out here. He pointed to the chair and said, "Go ahead, man. Have a seat."

I hesitated.

"It's cool," he said. "Welcome home."

*Welcome home.* A punch in the gut.

I stiffened. I'd heard those words before, but this time I actually *felt* them. Strange. Time to choose.

# Six

I pulled the chair into the shade. I'd had enough of the hot sun to last me lifetimes. Sat down as the guy grabbed the pitcher and filled one of the empty glasses. Pushed it towards me.

"Sweet tea."

I sat motionless, almost. Eyes back and forth between the guy and the tea. I'd already had a couple of beers for breakfast. I skipped the tea.

"Name's Mitchell," said the guy. "The m-60 was my side-kick for seven months in Vietnam. This got me an early-out."

He held up his left 'hand'. A metal hook.

I looked at the shiny metal and started remembering things I didn't want to remember. A couple of deep breaths to focus.

"Name's Eric," I said.

"Pleased to meet you, Eric."

I nodded. Took another deep breath. Then decided to take a chance.

# Seven

"People think my problem's in here," I said, tapping the side of my head.

"Brain damage?"

"No. Your good ole readjustment problems."

Then I swallowed hard and took another chance. Swept my hand in a wide arc around me and said, "How in the hell are you supposed to readjust to a bunch of civilians who don't know and don't give a damn about what you've been through?

One day I'm in a foreign country dealing out death and destruction while at the same time trying to protect my buddies by not getting *myself* blown to pieces. Next thing I know I'm back here in the good ole US of A watching some lady on TV bitchin' about how hard life is because she ran out of fabric softener.

Hell, I feel like a stranger in my own country. For years I wanted to go back over there just to kick some more ass. At times it's so bad I don't know if I can keep the lid from blowing off."

I turned and looked down the street. Waited. Then turned back to Mitchell.

"Plus I felt *alive* in combat," I said. "This civilian world is fucking flat-lined."

Mitchell nodded in understanding.

"I hear ya. Mind-numbing shopping malls are no replacement for a heart-poundin' firefight. Going back would also let you get payback for your dead and wounded. There's also a strong feeling of purpose and pride being with your unit. And that's definitely something you don't get back here while standing in line at McDonald's with a bunch of strangers. Facing the here-and-now is the real test. The tricky part."

"Tricky?" I said. "How in the hell do I 'readjust' after the crazy shit I went through? How in the hell do I 'readjust' while *still* carrying around a shit-load of crazy? I just want my old self back. I want my old life back. How do I do that?"

"With help," said Mitchell. "That's how." He paused and gave me a hard stare. "But get one thing straight real fast, soldier. I knew the first time I laid eyes on you that you were never going to be the person you were before you went in. That person is *his-tor-ry*."

He leaned forward.

"Eric, it's time for a new identity. You learn to face the person you are now, or you're in for a world of hurt."

Feeling pain close in from all sides, I lowered my eyes and looked down at the desk.

"Already there," I said.

Mitchell's eyes relaxed, and he looked at me a long moment.

"I hear ya, bro. I hear ya."

A Shitload of Crazy

# Eight

A tiny foreign car cruised by, pounding the neighborhood with its sound system. Summer heat baked the sidewalk.

Mitchell sat thinking, collecting his thoughts.

"As far as civilians are concerned," he said, "most of 'em aren't interested. Too far away from their world." He chuckled. "Of course, until they need the Guard in their home town because it just got trashed. Otherwise, it's just the way it is. That's why I opened up Mitchell's. Safe place where veterans, any war, any age, men and women, can hang out, talk, and support each other. And we've got vets comin' in here who never got near a battlefield. Just got caught up in the complicated gears of a giant war machine and came out slightly bent and off balance. Others just want to be here to offer support. A few civilians, too. Even got some counselors who volunteer a little time each week. But if you're really hurtin'," he added, tapping the side of *his* head, "we'll get you to the heavy-duty professionals, no problem."

I raised an eyebrow in doubt.

"I know, Eric. I know. Sure, the system has problems. What system doesn't? But there are islands of hope in every storm. There are always people that know the ropes, are good at what they do, and can really help. Take the Vet Centers, for example. They were founded by Vietnam veterans because they needed help fast. Ended up puttin' the centers out in the neighborhood, closer to the 'front lines'. Easier connections and less hassle. They even get separate money from Congress, so they've got a life of their own. And places like this?" said Mitchell looking around him, "Another new idea. We take the healing even *deeper* into the neighborhood."

# Nine

"Behind all this," he said, "is a very important point. Psychological wounds have nothin' to do with how brave you are. We're all human, not some race of super-heroes. We've all got chinks in our armor. I've seen some of the toughest bruisers in the army report for sick call and damn near pass out at the sight of an incoming needle.

But psych wounds are different. Can't just slap a field dressing on 'em. They can be sneaky and hard to pin down. Spooky, too, because *nobody* knows who's gonna be next. Don't forget though, if you didn't have intestinal fortitude, you wouldn't have been over there in the first place. So mental or physical, big or small, a wound is a wound. Just bite the bullet and treat it accordingly."

Mitchell looked at me for another long moment.

"Eric, you're a wounded warrior. Simple as that." He paused. "And wounds *can* be healed."

# Ten

I sat there stressed and relieved at the same time. Stretched in two directions at once and not knowing how I felt in the middle.

And Mitchell could be a talker.

"Eric, as you're discoverin', comin' back home can be a real bitch. And fightin' ain't easy, either. We're told we're fightin' for a just cause. Well, the guy you're lookin' at through the sights of your weapon was told the same thing. We've been honored for faith, loyalty, and bravery. Betrayed by greed, cowardice, and incompetence. We've died for truth. We've died for lies. We kill people. We break things. That's our job. It's what we do. Toughin' it out in the ultimate contest. And did we see and do things we wished we hadn't? You bet. Do innocent men, women, and children die? Damn right. Let's face it. War can be downright ugly. But until we get to the point where we can settle our differences peacefully, we're stuck with the ugly part. Plus, everything we were taught about right and wrong as we were growin' up? Right out the fuckin' window. So where does that leave us? Glad it's over, for one thing. Except for some of us, it ain't that easy. Buried feelings can poison our lives for years, and we don't even know it. Don't even see the damage bein' done. Other times we may suddenly find ourselves posin' for a mug shot in our local cop shop. Then we *know* our train has jumped the rails. And these feelings don't go away by themselves. They need to be dug up and defused. That's why *we're* here. To help each other deactivate 'em." He paused again. "And Eric?"

I waited.

"We're only as strong as our desire to help others."

# Part II

# Eleven

My M4 carbine fired around eight hundred rounds per minute. My paintbrushes didn't shoot at all. When I first got back to the States, I stood in my studio and picked up one of those brushes. It felt good to be back and downright decent to be holding something that didn't spit out death at a high rate of speed.

Short-lived feelings, though. Things change. Guaranteed.

I'd never paid much attention to what was going on in the world before I signed up. Walked around with my head in the clouds most of the time.

Lived in Boston all my life. Married my childhood sweetheart and landed a job as a high school art teacher. Painted seascapes in my spare time. But something was missing in my life. Some kind of spark. Thought those TV ads the army put out were pretty slick.

So, I enlisted, searching for adventure.

Found it.

# Twelve

Nothing like total strangers throwing jacketed rounds and explosive ordinance at you.

But my training brought out strengths and skills I didn't know I had. My head may have been in the clouds before I enlisted, but war did an outstanding job of drying me out behind the ears after I signed on the dotted line. As a result, I turned out to be a half-decent warrior. Learned what it was like to become a vital member of a team and got up close and personal with the true meaning of integrity and camaraderie.

A bullet in my right thigh earned me a purple heart. A bronze star for helping a buddy out of a tight spot. Decorated warrior. Honorable discharge.

And then, a one-eighty. Found myself alone and exposed in a land of civilians.

# Thirteen

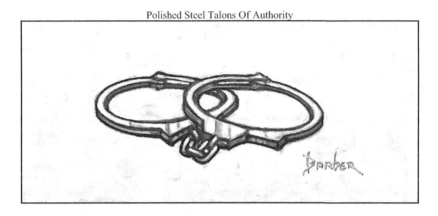

The handcuffs were tight. Polished steel talons of authority. The pulsing blue light from the light bar on top of the police car was hypnotic. Seeing double added to the show.

Cool. Had a good buzz going.

Didn't last, though. Woke up in jail. Being my third arrest for drunk and disorderly since I got out of the army, I knew what was coming next.

The TV in the cellblock came on. It had started. A full day of screaming game shows, dripping soap operas, and bellowing ads. All at high volume. Talk about cruel and unusual punishment…

And then, once again, the memories came flooding back.

It had been a tough deployment.

Actually, it was insanity. The women and children haunted me the most. Terror-stricken and tear-filled eyes. Wails of despair. The dead. These thoughts were quickly followed by the usual question.

What the hell was mankind's problem?

Ever since it came down out of the trees and picked up a stick, it's been beating its own brains out with it just so it can go on a little R&R, come back, and do it again. And it's *still* swinging that bloody branch around. Only now there are nuclear warheads tied to the end of it. Atomic *bombs*. Medieval mentality, 21st-century technology.

What the hell's going on? Does it ever end? And like, why am I even here? I want to feel like I matter. There has to be more to life than working, paying bills, and killing people. But what?

More questions. I wanted answers.

Medieval Mentality, 21ˢᵗ Century Technology

# Fourteen

As I said, when I first got out, it felt good to be back. But it didn't take long for the shit to rise. Anger. Anxiety. Depression. Thought going back to work might help. Keep the memories pinned down, keep me out of trouble, and out of jail. So, I asked for my old teaching job back.

It was a close call.

The school board labored long and hard in making a decision. My behavior worried them. When I showed up for my interview with a broken nose and two black eyes, they froze like deer in the headlights. But I insisted that I was turning my life around and cleaning up my act.

Took a while, but they gave in. I'd served my country and paid my dues. They also hoped a steady job would knock the sharp edges off my attitude. Smooth things out.

And even though things were rough on the inside, I hadn't changed much on the outside. I still kept my sandy brown hair short. Strong nose and brow. Gunmetal, grey eyes. One new thing was a pierced ear with a small, silver earring in the shape of a human skull.

People didn't ask me about it very often.

The school board wasn't thrilled with the earring but let me wear it.

The job helped, for a while.

# Fifteen

But after a few months, the pressure of the job responsibilities started to get to me. Paperwork. Meetings. Office politics. I had trouble staying inside the lines with my crayon, so to speak. At the end of a busy day in late fall, I sat down at my desk, stared out the window, and pondered.

War doesn't give you time to sort out your feelings. Just dumps a load of them on you all at once. But if you want to stay alive, you stuff 'em and get back to paying attention.

And if you make it, you come back a different person.

*Maybe like me. Stuffed, simmering, and emotionally numb.*

It wasn't long before I found out I was carrying around my own private platoon of personal demons and didn't know it.

It happened in the local supermarket. I was bouncing an apple up and down in my hand trying to decide how many to buy when I realized that the red of the apple reminded me of the color of blood.

When the thought of blood popped into my head, my demons saw a perfect opportunity and made their move.

Ambush in the produce aisle.

# Sixteen

It was that ambush that pushed me over the edge. Nightmares and flashbacks landed hard.

My drinking got worse.

Mistress alcohol. Knew her well. A great date before I enlisted. Party hardy. And while I was in, she was never far away. So, when I got out it seemed only natural to take a break, give into her siren song, and fall into her open arms in a major way. Little did I know at the time how long her bloody nails were and how deep she'd sink them into me.

In the meantime, it wasn't long before I lost my job. Too unstable, they said. The next ten years were spent under the influence and out of touch.

Scraped by on disability and money from a little drug dealing. As far as drugs go, of course, had to test the product. And there was some nasty shit out there. But hey, it brought in money, and money bought the beer. With a police escort, two visits to detox. *Not* the place to take a date.

My wife was scared. The man she married just never came back. She put up with me for seven of those ten years. That was all she could take. She left and moved in with her sister. Divorce followed, and it sucked.

Then three more years in a downward spiral. *Did* manage to stay out of jail, though. Just stuffed the pain deeper. Either that or when I thought I couldn't stand it anymore, I'd find some empty woods and scream face-down into the dirt for all I was worth and then sob until I was drained. I called it my little dance with the Devil. But it was only a matter of time before the pressure would build again, and I'd step back out onto that dance floor of darkness for another go-round. But finally, I'd had enough.

No more.

*Time to die.*

That was the day I met Mitchell.

\* \* \*

20

And so began a series of visits that would take me through an emotional obstacle course that would test my strengths in darkness, offer inspiration to light my way, and change my life forever.

Downward Spiral

# Seventeen

Three A.M. I was sitting on the edge of the bed letting my heart rate and breathing return to normal. Nightmare, nothing new. Reached out and grabbed a beer from the bedside table. Popped the top and took a swallow.

With a deep sigh, I looked around the room.

The window was open. Curtains swayed easily in the cool night air. Moonlight painted the hardwood floor with pale light.

Another slug and I stood up, walked over to the window, and stared out at the sleeping city.

The meeting with Mitchell had somehow brought me back from the brink. Knocked the edge off. Felt like I was hanging on by my fingernails, but at least I was hanging on.

Mitchell told me to stop by any time if I wanted to talk some more. It was a chilling thought, going back there and opening up painful wounds. But his invite haunted me. I'd actually been recognized and accepted out in the hood for who I was. Felt like a door had briefly opened a crack, and a sliver of light had flashed in the darkness.

A strange but most welcome feeling.

Mitchell even shared some of his own personal stuff with me. After I told him about my wife leaving me, he said the same thing happened to him.

"On my second wife," he said. "Married brains this time, 'stead of tits. Doin' alright."

In spite of my stress, I had to smile.

Back in bed, I polished off the beer and stared at the ceiling as the alcohol went to work soothing my soul.

A cat yowled somewhere in the alley below.

Thought of my divorce.

*Hope he's getting more than I am.*

# Eighteen

I finally made it back to Mitchell's place. Only took two weeks of stalling, excuses, and an extra beer for breakfast before I got on the bus. Me and my faithful twelve-pack. Can't leave home without it.

Also had some other things stuffed in my backpack: field jacket, disposal poncho for shelter, beef jerky, and a good book to read. A Louis L'Amour western. Proper equipment, and all.

When I got there, the sky was heavy with grayness. Humidity clung like soggy wallpaper. Swollen clouds hung low.

Mitchell was sitting in the over-stuffed chair. His feet were up on the desk, and he was reading the morning paper. A striking blond sat next to him. She was filing her nails. Green eyes sparkled into mine. A hint of a smile. Despite the clouds, her summer tan glowed.

Hint Of A Smile

I grabbed one of the empty chairs and sat down.

"Good to see you again," said Mitchell with a genuine smile. "Eric, this is Tiffany. She's a looker and a hooker. High-class, though. Doesn't peddle her stuff around here. High rollers are deployed on *her* battlefield. Her brother was killed in Iraq, and she feels closer to him sometimes if she's hanging around here with the troops." He smiled again. "Not easy to do when she knows what's going through the mind of every guy here."

She looked at me with a disarming smile and said, "Mitchell's right. I just don't know what I'm going to do with all you boys."

I felt my cheeks turn red.

# Nineteen

"We also value *her* company," said Mitchell. "Because I got to tell ya, a civilian with an open mind *and* heart can make for some good medicine around here. And Tiffany's got compassion to spare."

"Thanks, Mitchy," she said. "This place *is* special to me. Shelter from the storm and no forms to fill out in triplicate."

Mitchell threw back his head and laughed.

"Tiffany, I can just see you laborin' over all the paperwork required in your line of work."

"Hey, old man," she said with a grin, "my profession is just as important as yours in this crazy world. On a sincerer note," she said, "I'm serious, though. This place *is* special to me. I miss my brother, and sometimes it's rough up there in those condos. Another thing I like about this place? One heart. That of the group. 'Band of brothers,' as Shakespeare said. Congregation of comrades." Standing up, she said, "Gotta scoot. Need my beauty sleep."

"Okay, Tiffany. Sleep tight."

"Nice to have met you, Eric."

"Same here."

Then, with surprising understanding in her eyes, she leaned forward and said, "Welcome home, soldier."

My heart thudded at her honesty.

"Th-thank you."

"And you listen to ole Mitchy here. He's done his homework and has a magical touch in a crisis."

"I'll do that," I said.

Then she walked to a nearby Mercedes, got in, and drove off.

# Twenty

Cool breezes swept the streets. Thunder grumbled in the distance.

"Quite a lady," said Mitchell looking down the street where Tiffany had disappeared. Turning to me, he added, "And Eric, it *is* good to see you again."

"Same here," I said as I reached into my pack and took out a beer. "I think."

Mitchell nodded in understanding.

"Budweiser. Breakfast of champions, eh?"

"Yeah," I said looking down at the can with mixed feelings. "Guess so."

The first drops of rain started a light tapping sound on Mitchell's paper. He squinted up at the clouds and said, "Come on in. Coffee's waitin'."

I put the beer back and helped him spread some tarps on the outside furniture. Following him inside, I noticed a sign above the door:

> *"The soldier above all others prays for peace, for it is*
> *the soldier who must suffer and bear the deepest*
> *wounds and scars of war."*
>
> *General Douglas MacArthur*

"He's got that right."

"What was that Eric?"

"Oh nothing. Just mumbling."

The storm hit, curtains of rain wrapped the city in heavy grayness.

# Twenty-one

Mitchell's Place was one room. Plate glass windows faced the street. Mitchel walked up to one and looked out at the rain.

"City needs a good hosin' down once in a while."

But my attention was more on what was going on inside.

The two side walls of the room were used to tack up photos of guys in combat gear and an assortment of unit patches and campaign maps.

The rest of the place was a mixed bag. A couple of mismatched tables. One overstuffed sofa that matched the chair outside. A table in front of the sofa held a collection of magazines. A small bookcase beside it looked well stocked. Along the back wall stood a small fridge and a counter with a toaster oven, hot plate, microwave, odds and ends of kitchen utensils, and a small sink. Next to the sink, a door I found out later led to Mitchell's apartment.

# Twenty-two

There were two other people inside. One was standing at a pool table in the center of the room, racking up the balls. Little under six feet, solid, with a controlled energy about him. Quick brown eyes. Nervous twitch at the outside corner of his left one.

Mitchell turned from the window and looked at the pool player.

"Hey Jerry. This here's Eric."

"Welcome home, Eric. Back for repairs?"

"Say what?"

"Like that picture over there," he said pointing to a poster hanging above the sofa.

I walked over and took a closer look. It showed a painting of what looked like a small spacecraft kind of limping its way up towards a much bigger and healthier looking one. I turned back to Jerry.

"That's the title of it," he said, "'Back for Repairs.' The small ship is us veterans coming in to get our heads screwed back on straight."

"Hadn't quite thought of it that way," I said, "but yeah, I see what you mean."

There was another poster hanging next to it. Showed another ship flying out of the clouds.

"What's this one?" I said.

"It's called, 'The Return.' Shows us vets returning *after* repairs."

Back For Repairs

The Return

Fun to look at, but just thinking about the kind of repairs that might be waiting for *me* somewhere down the road made my stomach churn and my hands sweat.

Mitchell laughed and said, "Don't mind Jerry. He's our favorite science guy. Likes to let his mind wander."

"Hey, dreamers are important," he said. "Wouldn't have C-4 without 'em."

"Jerry was a demolitions expert," said Mitchell. "Likes to blow things up."

Jerry grabbed a cue stick and chalked it.

"Boom," he said, with a mischievous glint in his eye.

I could see this guy juggling blasting caps while whistling a tune at the same time.

# Twenty-three

The second guy was wearing a suit. His name was Jim. Mitchell introduced him as a member of a group of business leaders in the Boston area.

"Every one of them is a veteran," said Mitchell, "and be it time, money, or resources, their goal is to help groups like ours so we can turn around, reach out, and help other veterans."

"It takes guts to go to war," said Jim. "It also takes guts to open up and face the emotional crap we bring back with us. And that's why we're here. To cover your backs like you would have covered ours. Plus, if we've got vets working for us who want to come here and talk during working hours, we work out a schedule and give them paid time off. It helps all of us get some meaning back in our lives."

I also learned that business leaders like Jim all across the country were using the Internet to connect the hundreds of places like Mitch's so veterans could quickly find the nearest place to start looking for help. Vets helping vets. Plus, magazine articles, newspaper, and TV to cover this expanding network of support; even bumper stickers.

"We wear these," said Mitchell, holding up a camo sash with the American flag on it, "to identify ourselves as we comb the streets looking for homeless veterans. We call it retrieving the lost. We also go door-to-door asking if anyone knows of a veteran who may need or can offer help."

"A developing movement," said Jim, "that we're proud to be a part of."

Retrieving The Lost

# Twenty-Four

After Jim left, making a mad dash in the rain for his car, Mitchell and I grabbed a table in a back corner with a good view of the room and front door. Hot coffee and jelly doughnuts. I suppressed a growing thirst for beer and leaned hard on caffeine and sugar.

"Because war's the ultimate game," said Mitchell. "Life and death. Down and dirty."

I had just asked Mitchell why war seemed never-ending in human history. It turned out that he'd done a lot of research into human nature since his 'high school senior trip' into the jungles of Vietnam. He said it's what kept him sane after being hit.

"Some game," I said.

"Yeah," said Mitchell holding up his hook and giving it a close look. "Does get kind of rough around the edges."

High School Senior Trip

# Twenty-five

Mitchell's research into mankind's behavior officially began when his hand took a long ride on a hot piece of flying shrapnel. He said that he had to know what was going on in the minds of men that keep us at each other's throats all the time.

He wanted to know why we just can't be cool and take care of each other.

"Come up with any ideas?" I said.

"Yeah. In addition to war being the ultimate game, as long as there are those who love to play at it, it ain't goin' nowhere."

Despite the brutality of war, I had to admit the spirit of battle made me feel alive like nothing else did. It woke up something deep inside me that felt old beyond measure. Ancient. Primeval. Something that rose to the surface with a fiery passion and love of freedom that left everything else in the dust.

The loud crack of the cue ball making the break filled the room.

"Boom," smiled Jerry.

Outside, thunder crashed.

# Twenty-six

"Close one," said Mitchell looking out at the storm again. After the thunder rumbled off into the distance, he took a sip of coffee, put the cup down, and added, "You know guys, Plato once said only the dead have seen an end to war."

"Well, that doesn't sound very promising," I said.

"Sounds like job security to me," said Jerry, stopping to chalk his pool cue.

"Ya got that right," said Mitchell. "Guaranteed employment for every patriot, profiteer, liberator, mercenary, and thrill seeker."

"Sounds kind of grim," I said.

"Eric, the beast is in our blood."

"Say what?"

"It's true," he said. "The beast *is* in our blood. Hell, violence is in our *genes*. Throw a strange rat into another nest, and the newcomer will be torn to shreds because he's different. Even bacteria fight to protect their own. It's *instinct* that makes us fight. So it doesn't matter if it's religion, politics, skin color, or even if you talk different or dress funny. If you're different, watch out. You're a potential enemy. And the beast is always there, always on standby. May seem like it's sleepin' sometimes, but it can open its eyes at any time and start lookin' around for trouble. And there's always some of that to be found. As far as war goes, there's any number of things that can light a fire under its ass and get it raging. Next thing you know it's plowin' up the landscape like a Great Plains twister comin' right at ya."

Comin' Right At Ya!

# Twenty-seven

"And fighting to protect those we love," he said, "has always been good at lighting that fire. Only natural. I just mentioned political and religious differences. They're also great at settin' us off. Then there's just plain lust for power. Sounds crazy, but even boredom with peace can get us goin'. Plus, greed for the spoils of war is also a favorite. Fattens the wallet."

"But I wasn't after the spoils of war," I said. "At my send-off, I thought I was fighting for my country. I learned fast though, when the shit hit the fan, I was fighting for the men at my side."

"You and me both," said Mitchell. And we fought the good fight. Too bad the politicians can't get their act together *before* the killin' starts."

"Ain't that the truth?" said Jerry. "Probably don't have the balls to tackle the problems of peace, first."

"Either that," I said, "or they're making too much money from the arms dealers to stop the fighting."

"Combination of both," said Mitchell. "But you've got to admit, other times there just doesn't seem to be any other way of dealing with unhinged people and the harm they cause. They've got to be stopped somehow."

Jerry and I looked at each other and nodded in agreement.

"And," said Mitchell, "that's what warriors are for: to accept the challenge." He paused and stared into the distance. "But once we're standing there looking the beast in the eye, and once the action starts, we step into a world that can change us forever."

\* \* \*

With those words and ideas tumbling through my head, I decided to bow out and hit the streets for the rest of the day once the rain stopped. Took a while, but it did, and the storm moved on. Not so the turbulence inside my head. By the time I got back to Mitchell's for my next visit, I had one question burning in my mind.

# Twenty-eight

"So, what are we supposed to do?" I said. "Seems like there's got to be some way for mankind to smooth things out instead of constantly jumping from the frying pan into the fire."

I was sitting at a table with Mitchell, hot coffees in front of us. Jerry was at the counter pouring himself a cup. When he heard my question, he came over and sat down.

"This I'd like to hear," he said.

Mitchell thought for a minute and said, "Einstein told us you can't solve a problem with the level of intelligence that created it. Well, guess what? The way we've been poundin' on each other throughout history sure as hell supports *that* idea."

"Like I just said, what do we do?" I said.

"Elevate ourselves and find a new way of looking at things. And you can start by helping others. Do this and you automatically help yourself, and things will fall into place from there."

"That *sounds* good," I said. "But we still keep killing each other."

"That's right. It's what we've been doing ever since we learned how to pick up a stick and hit someone with it."

*That bloody branch, again,* I thought.

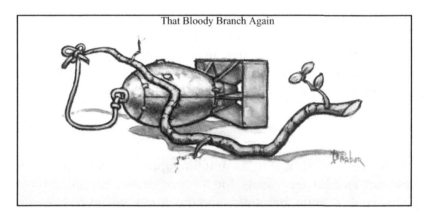

That Bloody Branch Again

"But why?"

"Bottom line?" said Mitchell. "Because we're asleep."

"Asleep?"

"Oh, there are a few enlightened souls out there, keeping the flame lit. But basically, the world's in a spiritual coma."

40

I wasn't tuned into this spiritual stuff. I knew if I drove a truck into a brick wall at high speed, there'd be little doubt as to what *my* reality was made of. But the spiritual world was always a little too flimsy for me to grab onto. Never gave it much thought. Figured I'd take a stab at it now, though.

"Spiritual coma?"

"Yeah. Way out of touch with our capacity for compassion, kindness, and caring. Things like that."

Didn't take me long to agree with that.

"No argument there," I said.

# Twenty-nine

"You see," said Mitchell, "everyone wants to be accepted for who they are. We need that kind of respect. It's important, pretty vital, actually. Because without respect, there's going to be trouble. But because mankind is asleep, we keep wanderin' around in a fog constantly bumpin' into each other and annoyin' the hell out of each other by claiming that *we're* the ones goin' in the right direction, and *we're* the ones with the right answers, and *our* religion is best. Just a sideshow of battlin' beliefs. The result? Just turn on the news and look at the mess."

"Seen enough of that already," said Jerry.

"Likewise," I said.

\* \* \*

More words and ideas. Getting heavy, though. Bowed out once again and hit the streets.

Beer for lunch. And supper. Maybe a few drugs for dessert after the evening meal. Balanced diet . . .

# Thirty

Until I met Mitchell, I was pretty much holed up at my place for years. Layin' low and keeping my distance from people. Except of course when hittin' the bars at night. But being out in public during the daytime and getting into deep conversations were putting a real strain on me. Too much to think about.

So I backed off for a while.

Eventually, I started making return trips. There were always people coming and going, and most of the time I'd just sit and listen. After a few weeks, I started getting more comfortable being there. Felt safe.

And of all the people I met there, Mitchell, Jerry, and Tiffany were the three I became the most relaxed with. Started to feel like a tight little unit.

And then came the day I dreaded but knew was waiting for me.

# Thirty-one

It started with another conversation about mankind being asleep. It had also been a while since my last breakfast beer, and my body was letting me know it.

"So what are we supposed to do about this spiritual coma we're in?" I said.

"Good question," said Mitchell. "But until all the answers are in, I'm puttin' my money on the dude they nailed to a tree."

I just looked at him.

"You talking about Christ?"

"Yup. He's the one. Anyone who can turn water into wine has my vote. But to me, as far as the rest of the world goes, somethin' is definitely missin'. It's kind of like a bunch of hyperactive kids from a bunch of different neighborhoods all runnin' around the same parade ground at the same time, slingin' dogma at each other."

"And what's dogma?"

"Opinions and viewpoints. My way is better than your way. That kind of thing. That's what I meant about different religions and their battlin' beliefs. Strangles the spirit. Our souls need room to move around and grow. Lock us in the dungeons of dogma and we're screwed." He paused. "Plus, there's just plain old confusion about who God is."

"There is?"

"There is. In the New Testament of the Bible, Christ gives us a Father of love and forgiveness. In the Old Testament we're told about a god who claims to be jealous, vengeful, crams war down our throats, and orders the killing of innocent men, women, and children, even infants, just because He's had a bad day."

My eyebrows went up with this one. I looked at Mitchell longer this time and said, "I thought God was supposed to be the good guy."

"I hear ya, Eric. Been buggin' me for years. Ever since this."

He held up his hook.

Dungeons Of Dogma

"Well, He must be have done something right," I said. "He's got a pretty big audience."

"Oh, I'm not saying there's not a good salesman tangled up in this somehow. I'm just saying there's a pretty big disconnect someplace. Because there's either one character out there who's schizophrenic, or we're talking about two, totally different folks."

*Schizophrenic? Two different folks?* My thirst for a cold one was *really* kickin' in now.

# Thirty-two

"There is one thing I *am* sure of," said Mitchell, "and that is the Old and New Testaments were written hundreds of years apart by a whole bunch of different people tellin' a whole bunch of different stories. Some are right-on. Some are far-out. A real mixed bag. And then there are all kinds of different ideas about what's goin' on in the *same* story. Plenty of room for confusion."

"Well," said Jerry, "you said we've got to find a new way of looking at things. A new angle. Maybe somewhere in all this confusion, the Old Testament god was just a visitor."

Mitchell was used to Jerry's scientific and imaginary wanderings. But this sounded kind of different.

"Okay, Jerry," he said. "Where are ya comin' from this time?"

"Just what I said."

This got me curious, too. "What do you mean, visitor?" I said.

"You know. As in, ancient astronaut."

"Ancient astronaut? Like, from outer space?"

"Where else?" he said with a big grin.

I looked Jerry straight in the eye, and my brain came to a screeching halt.

# Thirty-three

That's it! Time's up. Ancient astronauts were gonna have to wait. The only ancient thing I wanted in my life right now was a low level of alcohol in my bloodstream. Time to get it back up where it belonged.

I kept looking straight at Jerry and said, "Hold that thought."

"Sure thing," he said, a puzzled look on his face.

My backpack was sitting on the floor beside me. Reached down into it and grabbed a beer. Held it in my hand. Stared at it.

Mitchell was watching me and said, "I used to have that monkey on my back."

I tensed. Felt a lecture coming on. I'd heard them all before. As I said, this was the day I dreaded . . . face-to-face with a most outstanding lover. Trouble was, she was a lover determined to kill me.

Didn't matter. My defenses went up. Mistress alcohol was my savior. Soother of all stress and pain. Abandoning her seemed unthinkable.

Fear burrowed deep into my gut and held on tight.

*Would I quit? Can I quit? And what about my other drugs?*

And then something deep inside me shifted. This time something felt different. Mitchell, Jerry, and Tiffany. Felt like maybe I'd found a long-lost family.

I put the beer back.

"How'd you get rid of it?" I said.

"Dropped it like a hot rock," he said. "Got tired of it bitin' me in the ass all the time."

"Tough quitting?"

"You bet."

Mitchell gave me a steady look.

"Eric? We're here for you. Any time."

Those words hit hard and went deep. I knew this monkey would be the death of me if I didn't get rid of it. I also knew how real Mitchell and the gang were. One strong connection.

Then Mitchell's next words sealed the deal.

"Eric. Ya see that tree over there? Pretty little picture, right?"

He was pointing out the front window to a young maple tree sitting in a small, square plot of dirt in the sidewalk across the street.

"Yeah..."

"Well, I figure if that tree over there can grow, then so can I."
Without saying it, Mitchell just told me I also had what it takes.
*But even so...*

# Thirty-four

Despite my fears, the next thing I knew I felt the first crack open in the wall I'd spent years building around myself to keep out the pain. The pain of seeing a crumpled little body of a child lying face down in the dirt of a war-torn land. And of that child being swept up into the arms of its mother, whose accusing and grief-stricken eyes burned into my soul with the searing intensity of a white-hot flame.

But tearing down that wall was going to take a while, though. I'd been working on it for a long time, and alcohol and drugs were the cement holding the whole thing together.

*Then* I'd work on the emotional crap I brought back with me.

*Shit.*

# Thirty-five

Mitchell must have seen me struggling with this one.

"I know it's a big step, Eric. Growth is scary."

I looked at him and waited.

"One of the scariest things people can do."

"Scariest?"

"That's right. Fear of losing what you have throws cold water on the hope of getting somethin' better. But if you want to grow, you've got to leave behind your old ways of thinkin'. And that's a tough one. Because without realizin' it, we think holdin' on to the old ways is keepin' us safe. Keepin' us alive.

"But change means steppin' into new territory. Kind of like steppin' into a dark and unknown forest. And you know what lurks in dark and unknown forests, don't you?"

Hungry Animals And Little Green Men

"What?"

"Wild animals. The kind that tear you apart and eat you."

*Oh, great*, I thought. *Deep dark forests, wild hungry animals, and now, little green men.* And all this as my thirst for that beer in my pack just kept getting stronger.

"And that," said Mitchell, "means just thinkin' about change can raise the very real fear of death. You could say people are afraid to grow because they're afraid of dyin'."

Then Mitchell got up and opened a drawer under the back counter.

"Speakin' of change," he said rummaging through the drawer, "you'd be surprised how just fixin' yourself *in*side takes care of a lot of life's problems *out*side. And speakin' of the inside, Christ said we could do all the things He did, and *more*. Sounds wild, but everything we need is right in here," he said tapping the side of his head.

Finding what he was looking for, he pulled out a black t-shirt and tossed it to me.

"Here," he said.

Shook it out and held it up. Six words jumped out at me in stark, white letters: *"Growth is good. You go first."*

Looked back up at Mitchell. He was smiling.

\* \* \*

I drank the beer while waiting for the bus back to my place.

# Thirty-six

The next time I showed up at Mitchell's, I thanked him for his support and assured him I was taking his words to heart. It was morning and I was still kind of shaky, but at least I was there. Mitchell said just showing up was a good sign.

But I was also there because I was curious about what Jerry had said about that ancient astronaut stuff.

After Mitchell, Jerry, and I were settled at one of the tables, I tried to figure out how to start the conversation. It took a while, but I finally brought up the subject with my second cup of coffee.

"So, Jerry," I said with an uncertain look in my eye. "Ancient astronauts?"

I had hesitated.

He didn't.

"I ain't shittin' ya man," he said around a mouthful of doughnut. "There's a lot to it. Astronomers are discovering new planets around distant stars all the time. Our galaxy alone has a hundred billion stars in it, they think hundreds of billions of planets, and there are at least a hundred billion galaxies out there. To think we're alone is nuts. Even the Vatican is open to the idea of alien life."

"It is?"

"It is. Plus, the earth is just a newcomer to the neighborhood. The universe is old enough that there could be other races out there so far advanced they could stop by for a visit just by thinking about it. Hell, we've already set foot on the moon. Mars is next. From there, the outer planets and the stars. Then we may land on a planet someday, surprise the hell out of a bunch of primitive people, and they'll yell, 'Yikes! The gods are here!'"

Our Galaxy Alone

Yiles!  The Gods Are Here

# Thirty-seven

*Pretty bizarre*, I thought. I turned to Mitchell and threw him a questioning look.

He caught it and said, "Hmmm. There *are* a lot of books and TV shows about that kind of thing these days. But there's somethin' else that's had me wonderin' for years."

What's that?" I said.

"Thousands of years ago," he said, "it looks like a comet broke up and slammed into the eastern seaboard of the U.S. And when all those pieces hit, they created thousands of lakes and ponds. Actually, around half a million of 'em. They're called the Carolina Bays because most of 'em are out on the coastal plains of North and South Carolina. The coastal plains of the Carolinas are also the only place on this here planet where that meat eatin' plant, the Venus flytrap, is found on its home ground. So that got me to wonderin'. Did those little critters fly in on that comet? I mean, I hear comets have water and dirt in 'em. Great for a garden."

"Yeah," said Jerry. "All those nice, green lawns spread out across the front yards of America had to have come from someplace."

Mitchell looked at Jerry and frowned.

"What do you mean?"

"Scientists," said Jerry, "are telling us this planet was just a boiling hunk of lava when it was getting started. Once things cooled down, barren rock. No life. That grass seed had to come from *some*place. And if that grass seed came from someplace else, doesn't that mean, we did too? I mean, they also tell us the earth and everything on it, including the three of us, is made up of the dust of exploding stars. That means *we're* from outer space."

# Thirty-eight

"I don't know, Jerry," said Mitchell. "With this god mix-up thing goin' on, and now all these planets, I just don't know what to think. Until somebody can explain to me what's *really* goin' on, I'm gonna keep it simple: love thy neighbor, as much as possible."

Changing gears, and leaning hard on caffeine and sugar again, I said, "Nice thought. But do you really think love stands a chance in this screwed up world?"

"I do," said Mitchell. "But each one of us has to keep it as our own personal sidekick. Keep it out there walkin' point and clearin' the trail."

"How do we know which trail to head down?"

"I once heard about a sign hangin' over the front door of lamaseries in Tibet that says, '*A thousand monks, a thousand religions.*' Choose whatever path you're comfortable with. If your heart's in the right place, they all work."

I used to go to church once in a while, but when somebody told me there are over four thousand different religions in the world, I felt like I was standing on shaky ground and I could fall through any minute. Kind of like cruising down the strip when you're really hungry and not being able to figure out which hamburger joint to pull into. And now I'm hearing there's a different religion for every *person* on earth? Bizarre. But if my heart is in the right place…

Then I said, "Tibet?"

"Yeah. Whole different approach in the East. No agenda. No mind games. And no grumpy god and his personal baggage to deal with. The goal is harmony with nature and the universe. Keep it simple."

"Damn," said Jerry. "Harmony with the universe. Now *that* sounds like smooth sailing."

"It happened in Tibet," said Mitchell. "When Buddhism first arrived in that country, it was a great military power with all the blood, carnage, and sufferin' that goes with it. Next thing ya know, Buddhism turned it into the most spiritual and peaceful society on earth. But not us," he said, looking down into his coffee cup and shaking his head. "Slow learners." Then he turned to me and said,

"Did you know a reporter once asked Gandhi what he thought about Western civilization?"

"No. What'd he say?"

"He said he thought it would be a good idea."

# Thirty-nine

*A good idea.*

Those three words stuck to me like major Post-it Notes the rest of the day and into the night. And they stayed stuck. The next morning I felt like I was plastered with the damn things.

*A good idea. Get the message?*

I got the message.

So I bit the bullet and quit drinking.

And Mitchell was right. It *was* tough.

Detox again. The DT's this time. And the hallucinations were *not* something you'd see in a Disney movie.

But I made it out alive.

And after I got out, any other drugs I had left over from dealing hit the trash. Didn't need ugly temptations like those jumping out and surprising me. Turns out without alcohol and the corner drug store flowing through my veins, I was spending a lot more time at Mitchell's for moral support.

He and the crew were a big help. Occasional talk about the spiritual. Started to make some sense of it. Also got to talk to Tiffany more. Couldn't complain there.

So as time slid by, my craving for that cold one grew less, and my grip on sobriety got stronger. That's not to say I didn't drool when I walked by a bar and looked at a neon sign in the window advertising one of my favorite brews.

But Mitchell said my body's chemical confusion was settling down and kept using his favorite saying, 'Fake it 'til ya make it'.

Without alcohol to smooth out the bumps of life though, it kind of felt like someone had dumped a giant jigsaw puzzle of my life on the table in front of me, and all the pieces were the same color.

Going through those pieces, a few of them made sense. Some didn't. Some of them looked scary. I realized it was going to take a while before I dealt with each one and figured out where it fit.

# Forty

Plus Mitchell said if I wanted to talk to someone, but found myself alone, just writing down the bones would help.

Writing Down The Bones

"Write down the what?"

"The bones," he said. "Put words to paper. What was going through your head when your world was being turned upside down? How did it change your life, and how do you feel now about what you went through? The point is to let your feelings loose. Let 'em flow down your arm and right out the end of your pencil."

"My pencil? But I'm a painter, not a writer."

"Don't have to be. You can polish it up later. Or not. No problem. For now, all you're interested in is draggin' your demons out into the spotlight. They don't like the light. Steals their power. My grandfather owned a little bookstore for years. Told me if everybody wrote, there'd be no need for psychiatry. I tried it. It works. 'Course, I *have* spoken to a few shrinks. But the point is to get those feelings out in front of you where they can't sneak up on you and jerk you around. Then bring it in and share it with us if you want. The sharing wraps things up and lightens the load."

"And," he added, "you can paint it out, act it out, sing, or dance it out. They all work. Although writing is a good place to start because most of us already know how a pencil works."

So I tried it. Didn't get far. Same with painting. Too soon. Kind of felt like I was in an emotional straight jacket. Strapped in tight and buckled down hard by menacing memories.

But a new job *did* help. Part-time, pizza delivery driver. Since my social skills still needed some fine-tuning, figured I'd limit my contact with the general public. Still not in a talking mood. Zipping around town behind the wheel as a pizza-peddler was good for that - *Here's your pizza. Thank you.*

Wore my *Growth is Good* t-shirt, though. Got me smiles. Those were always welcome.

Growth Is Good

All things considered, despite the heavy stuff still lurking inside, I felt like I was on a steady climb upward.

But life would soon take care of that and bring me back down, hard.

# Forty-one

My head snapped around at the sound of screeching tires. I froze at the sound of the crash. The stunned silence *after* the crash grabbed my heart. The scream of a child stopped it.

I was waiting for the bus to Mitchell's when a car jumped the curb just up the street from me and slammed into a brick building. Broken glass showered the sidewalk. A lone hubcap rolled into the street, then fell and twirled on its rim with a wobbling, metallic sound before coming to rest with a final clunk.

The child screamed again.

Memories flashed.

The faces of war tore through my soul like lightning through a towering storm cloud. The sounds of war exploded in my mind like the storm's thundering roar.

My reactions were automatic. My cell phone jumped into my hand. I dialed 911 as I ran to the accident. The closer I got, the clearer things became. The driver was unconscious. A young man slumped forward, head resting on the steering wheel.

A young woman lay face down on the sidewalk, her dark hair covered with a ghostly shroud of cement dust from the shattered wall. A long, thin line of blood trailed across the sidewalk from her head and off the edge of the curb.

She'd been walking with her little girl when the car hit her.

Didn't see the little girl until I knelt beside the woman. She was standing in a near-by doorway desperately clutching a tattered doll to her chest. Wide-eyed, she stood frozen with fright, her mother no longer able to comfort her.

My mind reeled.

Snapped out of it when a paramedic cracked a capsule of smelling salts under my nose. Shook my head. Rubbed my eyes. Looked around. An ambulance was pulling away, siren echoing off the canyon walls of the city.

The mother was gone. The driver would make it. The little girl was safe.

I told the paramedic that I would be all right, stood up from the curb I'd been sitting on, and staggered back to my apartment.

# Forty-two

Trying to sleep that night was like trying to rub two ice cubes together to make fire. Didn't work. The sheets on the bed were a tangled mess. Nightmares were no problem. Sleep was impossible. Every one of my demons kicking the hell out of me made sure of that.

Once again, felt myself losing ground, *fast*.

*I need a drink.*

In a haze of despair, I found myself dressed and headed to the nearest bar.

# Forty-three

The room was crowded, but as the fates would have it, there was one empty barstool with my name on it.

"Get a grip, soldier," I mumbled to myself as I sat down, "and get yourself *out* of this place."

"Talk to yourself much?"

I turned my head and was greeted by a friendly smile.

"Bill, from Chicago."

I hesitated. Strange guy in a bar? But talking to someone might help. Managed to return the smile.

"Eric, from right here in Boston."

Bill had that tough, weathered look of someone who worked hard outdoors. Maybe a steelworker. One beefy hand was wrapped around the neck of a beer bottle. The other worked at peeling off the label. He looked happy to have someone to talk to.

He abandoned the label.

"Came to Massachusetts on sort of a vacation," he said. "Had to visit Concord where 'the shot heard 'round the world' was fired. That Revolutionary War was somethin', wasn't it? Rag-tag militia against the might of the British army. Got to hand it to those guys. You just mumbled somethin' about a soldier. You a veteran?"

I hesitated again.

"Army."

"Yeah? Me too. Combat?"

I nodded.

"Yeah? Me too."

*Keep talking, Eric. Stop thinkin' 'bout drinkin'.*

I ordered a shot of Jack Daniels.

# Forty-four

The bartender set an empty glass on the bar in front of me and poured the whiskey. With a desperate craving, I stared down into a world of trouble.

A World Of Trouble

"Hey man," said Bill. "You alright?"

I continued to stare into the glass and said, "My first drink in six months."

"Whoa there. Maybe you better…"

I turned and looked at Bill. He was only one man, but that still made two of us. A small group, but still a group. Tiffany's words about the safety and strength of the 'band of brothers' sent my demons crawling, scuttling, and slinking back into the shadows.

Just not fast enough.

*And just because they're hiding in the shadows, doesn't mean they're gone.*

The burn of the fiery liquid sliding down my throat was the last thing I remembered.

# Forty-five

"Hey, I think he's comin' around."

Fluorescent ceiling lights. Muffled voices. A shape bending over me slowly resolved itself into that guy in the bar.

"Bill?" I said. "What…where…?"

"Relax man, you're in the ER."

"The ER?"

"Yeah."

"What happened?"

"You lost it."

"What? How…?"

A nurse came over and adjusted an IV that snaked down into my arm. She smiled at me and then turned to Bill.

"A light sedative," she said. "We'll be keeping him overnight. Just to keep an eye on him."

"That's cool," said Bill. He looked at me. "At ease, man. You're in good hands."

Mission accomplished, the nurse turned and left.

Bill watched her go, then turned back to me.

"Man," he said. "When ya started throwin' back those shots, I knew ya wasn't gonna be sittin' on that barstool long. And I was right. I also knew there was some heavy-duty shit goin' on inside ya." He paused and then said with compassion, "I know the feelin', man. I know the feelin'." He paused again. "But anyway, when ya started topplin' over, I managed to grab ya just before your head hit the floor." He paused again. This time with a grin. "Good save, though. Even if I do have to say so myself."

A wave of anxiety rolled over me, and I groaned.

"Hey man," said Bill. "Hang in there. You can take it."

*Bill's the other half of the only group you've got right now. A life raft. Grab it.*

I took a ragged breath.

"I hear ya," I said weakly.

"Yeah. Whatever happens, happens. Just 'cept it."

"Just what it?" I said, trying to claw my way through the cobwebs of the sedative.

"'Cept it. You know, 'ceptance."

It finally sank in.

"Oh, you mean *ac*ceptance."

"Sure. 'Ceptance. It can change your whole life." Bill tried to snap his fingers. "Just like that. Did mine. After all, 'ceptance is heaven, resistance is hell."

I took another deep breath, offered myself up to the drug dripping into my arm, and drifted along with Bill's words.

# Forty-six

"Yup," he said. "Ya face whatever happens, whether ya like it or not. No whinin'. No opinions. No judgin'. Just look it right in the eye. Hardcore. Besides, when somethin' happens, in a split second it's history, and you can't change that. So anyway, for years my wife has been callin' me a drunk, an' I kept sayin', 'No way,' 'cause I was ashamed of the thought. Then one day, I was sittin' in a bar when a fella walked in an' said to the bartender, 'Hey, ya know it's hard work bein' a drunk. Tryin' to almost kill yourself every day takes a lot out of ya.'"

Despite the fog in my brain, I could see he had a point there.

"So I sat there," said Bill, "drinkin' an' thinkin' about that for quite a while. Then when I finally got up to leave, I walked out the door and fell flat on my face." He took a breath. "All of a sudden there I was lyin' there with my face on the sidewalk, gettin' a real close look at it, an' I realized 'cause o' where my face was, I *must* be a drunk! So I 'cepted it."

Bill flashed a bigger grin.

"Hey, I'm still a drunk, but now I got no more shame."

I looked at Bill through hazy eyes and managed a weak smile.

"Thanks, bro."

"Sure. No problem."

# Forty-seven

*Just because they're hiding in the shadows doesn't mean they're gone.*

Hiding In The Shadows

"You still with us?" said Jerry.

I blinked myself back into the world of Mitchell's place.

"Yeah. Yeah, I'm still here."

"Relapses are a dime a dozen," said Mitchell. "Just part of the rocky road. And flashbacks and nightmares? Just your soul letting you know it wants to heal."

"Couldn't it ease up a little?"

Mitchell chuckled.

"Not with the shit we throw at it."

# Forty-eight

"You're here with us now," said Tiffany. "That's all that's important."

It had been several days since my encounter with Mr. Jack Daniels. Tiffany, Mitchell, and I sat at one of the tables in Mitchell's place. Jerry was at the pool table but kept an eye on me at the same time. It was good to be back. Plus my boss at the pizza place was cutting me some slack.

"Thanks, Tiffany," I said.

But if relapses are common, I couldn't help but wonder when I might be ambushed again. She must have seen I wasn't very thrilled with that idea.

"Looky here sweetie," she said, reaching over and squeezing my hand, "you'll be fine. You can worry about tomorrow if you want to, but you don't have to. And besides, alcohol abuse puts you one step ahead of the game." She paused. "Well, for that matter, *any* kind of drug abuse puts you one step ahead."

"How do you figure that?"

"Most people cruise through life without facing that kind of storm. Without being pushed to the brink, without being forced to choose between life and death, they pass right by the entrance to the spiritual path without even seeing it."

Tiffany's words kind of put me at ease. Kind of. As far as standing at the entrance to any path was concerned, I just felt

Door Number 1, 2, or 3

confused. Didn't know if I was standing in front of door number one, two, or three.

But whatever my feelings were, they didn't last very long.

The front door of Mitchell's place slammed open.

# Forty-nine

I'd heard the faint rumble of a Harley out front earlier, but it didn't really register, until now.

The guy in the door was large, in leather, and pissed off. Anger radiated from him like the heat from the desert sun in July.

The guy's face was sunburned. His beard was parted in the middle from the wind and stuck out on both sides of his face. His hair was flared and tangled. But it was the fury in his eyes and the nine-millimeter in his hand that held us captive.

*Oh, man,* I thought, *and I just got* out *of the hospital.* But I soon discovered this wasn't about me.

The guy raised the gun and put it to the side of his head.

"I've had it," he said.

# Fifty

Time stopped.

Then I witnessed a bit of Mitchell's magical touch that Tiffany had talked about.

In one smooth movement, Mitchell held up his coffee cup in a gesture of greeting, smiled, and said, "Combine ingredients, shake well, and deposit at Mitchell's Place."

The guy blinked. He paused. He scowled, and then he laughed. Defused.

Minutes later, he was sitting at a table with Mitchell, talking in low tones. Two coffees stood between them. Two half-eaten jelly doughnuts.

Jerry, Tiffany, and I faded into the background to give them some space.

The guy's name was Shaggy, and he talked for quite a while. Mitchell didn't say a word. He just listened. Mitchell finally said something, and Shaggy said, "Moral injury?"

"A wound to the soul," said Mitchell, "when our basic sense of right and wrong gets blown away. An attack on the heart when things we experience don't fit with what we were taught as kids. Like how we're supposed to play nice and not hurt others."

Shaggy stared off into space.

"Done plenty of hurtin'."

Blinking himself back into the room, he said, "But I've got nothing against lightin' someone up if they're trying to do it to me. It's kill or be killed. That's the way the game is played. But terrorizing innocent families and killing innocent people *ain't* the way I was raised. Like you said, I was taught to be kind to others. Hell, I even shot dogs. Family pets. Shit, I *love* dogs."

"Goddammit!" he said. "Battles belong on fuckin' battlefields, not in someone's fuckin' living room. Didn't take long before I got to wondering who I was and why I was even over there.

"And I just can't shake these dark moods whenever I think of the looks in the eyes of . . . especially the women 'n kids. Feels like there's evil inside me for doin' the things I did, and it's using a big rusty hook to tear out my heart."

"I hear ya," said Mitchell with a deep sigh. "Some of the things we did were fucked, alright."

74

A heavy silence hung between the two warriors.

Then a frown suddenly creased Shaggy's forehead.

"Another thing's been buggin' me. When I shipped out, I thought God was supposed to be on my side. Ended up feeling abandoned by Him. Big time."

"Felt the same way," said Mitchell and gave Shaggy a quick overview of our 'Western' god and the Eastern search for harmony.

Shaggy stared off into space again with that one.

# Fifty-one

Mitchell looked at Shaggy a moment and said, "Shaggy, as far as I'm concerned, the 'evil' you think is inside you is just shame and guilt. Just normal feelings for what you went through."

*"Normal?"* said Shaggy turning to look back at Mitchell.

"That's right. The things you did in the past which haunt you today don't mean you're a bad person. In fact, the shame and guilt you feel are proof you *are* okay."

"Proof?"

"Yeah. If you didn't care about hurting others, you wouldn't have those feelings. It's the good part of you that's feeling bad about what you did. It's the goodness in you that's reminding you, even though it feels like punishment, that you're only human. And humans ain't perfect. So once you realize that you're basically a decent guy who was thrown into a shit-storm of ugly choices, it'll be easier, maybe not easy, but easi*er,* to find your way home."

"Damn," said Shaggy, shaking his head.

"And when you stop and think about it," said Mitchell, "we got a real good look at our dark side and what happens when we dance with it. We got a front row seat as to what that dance can do to our minds. Somethin' most people out there never have to go deal with. Although I think they'd be a lot healthier in the head if they did."

Shaggy scowled and said, "Wait a minute. *Our* dark side?"

"Yeah. We've all got one. Light and dark. Balance. Kind of like a yardstick. You need both ends of the stick to find out where you are in between. But anyway," said Mitchell. "When we're lost in the darkness in here," he said tapping the side of his head, "what we find in that blackness can sometimes help us get out of it. Kind of like that saying, 'When it gets dark enough, the stars come out.'"

"Starry nights sure as hell ain't what I'm thinkin' about when those dark moods hit me."

"I know, Shaggy. I'm trying to put the pieces together myself. I'll keep you posted. In the meantime, just recognize that the darkness is an important part of us, accept it, then move on to other things."

"Accept it? How in the hell do you accept something that can get that twisted?"

"Simple," I said. "Just 'cept it.

76

Shaggy looked up at me. I'd been walking by the table and couldn't help but overhear his question. I went on to tell him what Bill had told me about acceptance.

"And like Bill said, doesn't mean you have to like it. Just know it's there."

"Damn," said Shaggy again.

"There's another thing," said Mitchell. "If you don't respect the enemy as a warrior defending *his* beliefs, whether you agree with them or not, and if you don't honor him as a worthy opponent, you're going to have a hard time bringin' yourself home. Your respect for him, even if he's dead, will restore some of your own self-respect. The same goes for honoring the spirit of the civilian dead."

"Harmony, acceptance, honor, *and* respect?" said Shaggy. "Damn."

"Here," smiled Mitchell. "Have another doughnut."

# Fifty-two

Shaggy left a short time later after offering Mitchell heartfelt thanks and saying how he'd keep coming back to work on getting better. When he took off, the roar of his Harley had a stronger sound to it. A happier beast. Good to hear.

A Happier Beast

Sitting at the table with Tiffany and Mitchell, I told Mitchell that at first, it seemed like a pretty one-sided conversation between him and Shaggy.

"It was," he said. "In the beginning, don't talk, don't judge, and don't analyze. Leave the details for later. In the beginning, just listen. Just *be* there. Makes a big difference." He paused. "Something else to remember? We can never really know what another person is feeling. All you've got to remember is that pain is real."

"That's for sure."

After a few minutes, I turned to Tiffany.

"I've kind of had it, too. How about a change in scenery?"

A twinkle in her eye and a mischievous smile.

"Why the hell not?"

# Fifty-three

I'd spent many hours in the Museum of Fine Arts in Boston, under the influence. Now with a sober eye, I was enjoying a second look. Great escape without the hangover. Tiffany's presence added to the enjoyment.

As we passed a tour group, we weren't really paying attention until we were stopped in our tracks by the guide's words, "You want torture? It's yours. You want art? It's yours. Take your pick."

Tiffany and I moved in closer behind the tourists. I moved closer to Tiffany.

"George Bernard Shaw," said the guide, "believed that not honoring our creativity leads to trouble and tortured souls. Be it with individuals or whole societies.

"Because if we don't create in a *con*structive way and build things up, we'll create in a *de*structive way and tear things down. That's because creativity cannot be stopped, stifled, or stalled in any way. It has to be expressed *somehow*.

"Hitler was an extreme example of that 'somehow' spinning out of control and crashing hard. Because all he wanted to be was an artist. But his society said no. So, he got pissed off, created in a *de*structive way, and sadly took a lot of people down with him."

Eyebrows rose among sounds of surprise.

"Talk about a dark side," I said to Tiffany.

"Ya got that right."

"On the flip side," said the guide, "we can use that same creative power to heal. And art is one of the finest tools we have for doing just that. Stories are told of ancient civilizations fixing problems in distant provinces by fixing the music. Fix the music and everything would be restored to a healthy balance. Art heals," she said, "Plus on top of that, we're all artists."

More raised eyebrows.

"It's true. How many of you have heard the words, 'Look at the mess you created?'"

Subtle laughter drifted through the group.

"Exactly. That mess was *your* creation. *You* created it. And your masterpiece? Your *life*. Your very existence. Work or play, it's something you create on a moment-to-moment basis with every decision you make. Every single one." She paused. "Your life. Your art. What kind of painting are you going to paint?" She paused again and added with a smile, "But no sweat. As I said, art heals."

"Pretty intense museum guide," I whispered to Tiffany.

"Damn straight," she whispered back. "The creative part makes me think of some of my clients."

I held back a smile.

* * *

For the rest of the time in the museum that day, Tiffany and I looked at the paintings in a whole new light. In the quiet of our own minds, we also looked at our *lives* in a whole new light.

# Fifty-four

Several days later, Bill walked into Mitchell's place. Mitchell was washing some dishes, Jerry was at the pool table, and Tiffany and I were sitting at one of the tables flipping through magazines. When Bill saw me, a smile lit up his face.

"Hey, the patient's lookin' better."

"Feelin' it, too," I said, surprised but glad to see him again. "Not heading back to Chicago yet?"

"Naw. Decided to stick around a little longer. Sight-seein' an' see how you was doin."

"I appreciate that."

I introduced Bill all around. But he wasn't alone. Bill introduced a strange little man who had come in the door with him. The stranger's skin was dark. Long, white hair hung down to his shoulders. Laugh lines creased the corners of his eyes. A wide grin of sparkling, white teeth.

"This here is Ravi," said Bill. "Met him a few days ago. Says he was a soldier over in India. Did some mercenary work, too. So he's been around. Says he doesn't know where his white hair came from. Spent a lot of time up in those big mountains over there learnin' some far-out stuff. Once we got to talkin', I thought I'd bring him here. Seemed like the thing to do."

"Sounds good to me," said Mitchell. "Welcome."

"Thank you," said Ravi looking around. "Cozy lookin' digs."

"Thanks."

I pushed the tables together, and we all grabbed chairs and got comfortable. Coffees all around. Then Bill pulled a rabbit out his hat.

# Fifty-five

"So, Eric," he said. "After that night with you in the ER, I decided to jump on the wagon, too. Went out to the car an' dumped a brand-new six-pack into the trash."

Surprised, I said, "Congrats. Welcome aboard. What made you decide, then?"

"The nurse that was taken' care of ya told me that when we drink, it's *ethyl* alcohol that knocks us on our ass. Said if you take the water out of a glass of beer, whiskey, wine, or whatever, the gas that's left is a dead ringer for *ether*, your basic all 'round general anesthetic. An' it makes you act just as stupid."

"Ya think?"

Light laughter around the tables.

"Plus," said Bill, "my wife was always tellin' me I drank enough booze to float a battleship. So lookin' at you layin' there all messed up, I thought about what both she and the nurse said, and then saw where *my* life was headin' if I didn't change course . . . fuckin' shipwreck.

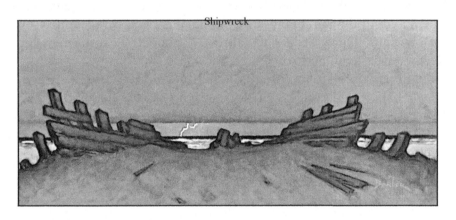
Shipwreck

An' that was that. Into the trash the beer went." He paused. "'Course, it's a little rough gettin' out of the startin' gate."

"Man, I hear ya on that one. But once again, congratulations. Good news is always welcome around here."

"Yeah, and Ravi said somethin' about me startin' out on a new path, whatever that means."

"Leave that six-pack in the trash long enough," smiled Ravi, "and you'll figure it out."

More light talk, but soon the conversation drifted into 'deeper' territory, and we discovered that Ravi had indeed, been around. With our encouragement, he started sharing some of the insights he'd bumped into 'up in those big mountains'.

# Fifty-six

"Ravi," said Mitchell, "the state of the world isn't lookin' too cool right now. With all the travelin' you've done and the things you've seen, have you got any thoughts on how you might help turn things around?"

Ravi thought for a minute and said, "I do. One of my favorite ideas, if I had the power, would be to set up a course in a universal sign language. Required. Worldwide. Kindergarten through college. Get everybody on the same page.

"Being able to travel anywhere in the world, and talk to anyone we want, would open our minds to the fact that every one of us has the same hopes and dreams. The same loves and fears.

"Using the simplest of signs, we could begin to heal the damage that's been done by the conflict-ridden policies of power hungry and narrow-minded politicians and religious leaders. We'd be able to see past what the *outside* of people look like and recognize that the same heart beats *inside* the chest of all of us."

With that, Ravi took a sip of coffee and silently looked around the group.

"Well," said Mitchell, "That's right to the point."

"Yeah," said Tiffany in a dreamy voice. "That would be nice."

# Fifty-seven

A Calmer World Beneath The Waves

"Then I'd go with meditation," he said. "Takes discipline, but it's pretty simple. Just sit down, shut up, and stop thinking. Knocks the snow off the antenna, sharpens the signal. You see your life in a healthier light."

"Sharpens the signal?" I said.

"Yeah. Kind of like tuning into a different radio frequency than the one we're used to. A more peaceful one. Lets you know a much calmer world exists beneath the stormy waves of life. Ritual helps, too."

"Ritual?"

"A change in routine that creates a comfort zone for you and gives you time to chill and recharge your batteries. A place you can keep going back to when you want to give yourself time to just 'be'. Like a walk in the woods, or maybe something more formal, like in a church. Anything that puts you at peace."

"As far as meditation goes," said Bill. "I thought the purpose of that was to empty the mind. But wouldn't an empty mind be prime real estate for dark memories of war to rush in, set up camp, an' make things even worse?"

"You don't really 'empty' your mind," said Ravi. "You just replace the jumble of daily thoughts with a calmness that carries over into your day-to-day life. Also helps you deal with your personal demons when you're ready."

My eyebrows kind of floated up with that one.

Ravi saw this and said, "I know, Eric. I'm not saying that part is going to be easy. Our memories are with us for life. It's just that when we're willing to work at it, we can meet those memories on a level playing field where they come over to our side instead of being on the opposing team."

"Sounds like work, though."

"It *is* work. But when ugly memories raise their head, remember, they're just that. Memories. Ghosts from the past." He paused. "And what's something all ghosts have in common?"

"You can put your hand right through them," said Mitchell.

# Fifty-eight

"Looks like those mountains kind of recharged your batteries," said Bill.

"Oh, that they did," said Ravi. "I meditated for months in a monastery. Got a look at the light behind the scenes."

"The light behind the scenes?"

"The light the Creator turned on for us.

Curious, Bill said, "Now that sounds like some special kind of light."

"Very special," said Ravi. "As your Bible story goes, in the very beginning there was nothing but darkness. Right?"

Bill kind of hesitated.

"Yeah…"

"Then came the command, 'Let there be light!' Right?"

"Yeah…"

"Well, when that light came on, poof, instant universe."

"Poof?"

"Yeah. I didn't want to get too technical."

"I don't think you did."

"Good. But yeah, so basically this light was used to get things cranked up and rolling and even today is still behind the scenes keeping things moving right along."

Tiffany was still daydreaming about a universal sign language when the word 'Creator' snapped her out of it.

"Wait a minute," she said looking at Ravi. "The Creator? Are you talking about that cranky ole guy with the long white beard who…"

"Oh, you're familiar with that one?"

"Yeah," she said looking down at the table with a deep sigh. "I am." Looking back up she added, "He's one of the reasons I hit the streets."

Ravi looked at Tiffany a moment and nodded his head in respect and understanding.

Then he said, "Tiffany? What I'm talking about is quite a bit different. *Real* different, in fact. Kind of like science fiction." He paused. "Just imagine a mind as big as the entire universe. A vast sea of creative energy that fills the whole cosmos and keeps it alive and kicking. And that includes us. Plus, it's where we came from in the first place."

"We did?"

"We did. As well as every blade of grass, tree, rock, mountain, planet, and star there is and anything else you can think of. And Tiffany? Using the word Creator is just one way of describing this energy. It's also been called the Great Spirit, the Light, and the All. In the Star Wars movies, it's called the Force. There are other names, too. But they're all names for the same creative power. A universal love shared by all of us."

This idea was big, and Tiffany's thoughts came alive and raced to catch up.

"Fact check," she said. "Fact check. I've heard all about this love idea before, but it never made any sense. If this Creator is so full of love, how can It allow so much pain and suffering to exist in the world?"

# Fifty-nine

Every Tree, Rock, And Star There Is

"Remember, Tiffany," said Ravi, "this isn't the romantic love that puts us through the wringer. This is energy. Pure and simple. Well, maybe not that simple. Energy with intelligence. A wee bit more intelligence than *we* can wrap our heads around. The point is, being *the* All, it *allows* all. Anything goes. And like a loving parent that must watch its child fall and skin its knee while learning to ride a bike, the All must wait for us to wake up and find our way back to It and the mysterious and magical world we came from. And when we get there, we're greeted by a feeling of vitality, joy, serenity, and peace. Home-sweet-home."

"Sounds good to me," she said.

*The ancient astronaut story was a tough one to get a handle on, but this universal think-tank idea was really testing me.*

In the meantime, Tiffany's mind had settled down and was cruising along comfortably now.

"Okay, I'm starting to get the picture," she said. "But there's something else I don't get."

"What's that?"

"You hear a lot of talk these days about some people being more 'sacred' or 'holy' than other people. But if we all come from this 'super-mind' together, then how can any one person be more or less 'holy' than anybody else?" She paused. "Seems like we're all in the same boat."

"We are," said Ravi. "Look at it this way. Think of a giant jigsaw puzzle as big as the universe with trillions and trillions of pieces in it, and you are one of those pieces."

"Big puzzle."

"It is. Now imagine removing that one piece which is you. What happens?"

"The puzzle is incomplete."

"That's right. That's because you are *essential* to the existence of the whole thing. You are *needed* to complete the picture."

As the thought of being needed sank in, long buried tears came to the surface and burned Tiffany's eyes.

Kind of burned my eyes, too.

"Tiffany," said Ravi in a gentle voice, "That means it doesn't matter if you're the president, the pope, a street sweeper, or a streetwalker, spiritually we all stand side-by-side on equal footing. There's no difference. No one is more or less 'holy' than anyone else.

And because the All is the source of all, the same goes for every different thing, place, and day of the year."

Tiffany sniffled, took a deep breath, and pondered all this. Suddenly there was a new sparkle in her eyes and a big smile lit up her face.

"Good to hear," she said. "I like it."

But Bill wasn't finished.

# Sixty

"Ravi," he said, "This is all interestin' stuff. But as far as this Great Spirit thing goes, are you sayin' we're *all* part of this 'Creator'? This 'All'?"

"Roger that," said Ravi, "You see, we know children inherit things from their parents. It's only natural. So here we sit with the ability to think about who we are, and thought suggests a mind. Well, we *know* we have minds, so it stands to reason we inherited them."

"Then that *would* make all of us rugrats of the universe," said Bill.

"Offspring of the All," said Ravi. "Sons and daughters of the Creator. We all inherit equally. No lawyers fighting over *this* last will and testament."

"Well, that's good to hear. But life doesn't seem to give us much time to get our act together before we eat dirt."

"Not to worry. When the Buddha finally got around to getting *his* act together, he remembered thousands of his past lives."

"Thousands? You mean like in reincarnation?"

"Yup. There's no rush. There's plenty of time to get your act together."

Bill thought about this for a minute and said, "Yeah. I kinda like the idea of just movin' on to the next base of operations when it's time. *Does* kind of take the pressure off." After a moment he added, "Yeah. I can go with that."

Movin' On

"As a warrior," said Ravi, "that puts you in good company."

"What do you mean?"

"Your famous general, George S. Patton, was also a believer. Says he remembers being a Roman legionnaire under Julius Caesar. Remembers fighting with Napoleon and being in combat in other lives, too. Said he'd come back again to lead armies. Personally," said Ravi, "I think Western society shot itself in the foot by getting rid of the idea. Without it, you're left wandering around feeling like you're stuck with this one chance, and if you don't get it right, you're screwed."

"Common feeling in the world today," said Tiffany. "No pun intended."

More shared smiles.

With all the trouble I'd been having with these spiritual and cosmic mind maneuvers, I hadn't said much. But I had toyed with this subject off and on over the years and finally felt like I had an opening into the conversation.

"So how come we don't hear more about this reincarnation stuff?" I said.

# Sixty-one

"Because," said Ravi, "the idea of reincarnation makes each one of us responsible for our own destiny. That means *we* decide our own future. And that's something a lot of religions don't want you to know about."

"Why not?"

Because they want you to come to *them* to be saved. They want you to think *they* hold your destiny in *their* hands. But if they went around telling you that *you're* in charge, they'd go out of business. No more donations. Empty collection plates. That's why the line, '*Come to us, do what 'we' say, and we'll save you from a vengeful God and eternal damnation,*' is such a popular game plan."

"Fear of God. Fear of death," I said. "Hell of a system."

"Ain't it though," said Ravi, "Especially after your Christ gave you a direct order to, 'Fear not...'"

We all looked at each other and pondered that one for a while. Then Bill looked at Ravi and said, "Our Christ? He's not yours, too?"

"Bill, in the Far East we have a whole different cast of characters reading from a whole different script. Different spiritual traditions, that's all. But we too, like you, are just looking for love."

Bill thought about that for a minute.

"Interesting..."

# Sixty-two

*Love,* I thought with a deep sigh. *So simple. So hard to track down.*

Then leaning back in my chair, I took another deep breath and brought my thoughts back to something much easier to find.

"Speaking of looking for things," I said, "I'm looking for some more coffee. My brain cells need recharging."

We were all in agreement, except Tiffany who said she had to leave soon.

Mitchell was about to get up for his refill when he stopped and looked around the room.

"And just think," he said. "All this just because the light got turned on."

"Long lasting light bulb, too," I said.

"Very long," said Ravi.

After we were settled back at the table, and the coffees had been adjusted and fine-tuned, my curiosity stirred again as I still struggled to get a grip on all I was learning.

# Sixty-three

"If we've got so much going for us," I said, "I still don't understand why the world is so messed up. And why are we doing such a lousy job of remembering where we came from in the first place?"

"Maybe if we remembered where we came from," said Bill, "and how 'heavenly' it is there, we might all tear-ass back there as fast as we could to get away from the chaos of *this* world."

"And the game would be over," said Ravi. "So we forget in order to keep the game going. But things *are* looking up. After all, we're already two vibrations above a rock."

"What?" I said.

"Mineral, vegetable, animal. We're animals, so that makes us…"

"I get it," I smiled. "I get it. But to say we're one jump ahead of a carrot doesn't sound very inspiring." Thinking about that straight jacket again, I said, "I know I'm making progress, and I know I'm out of the vegetable garden, but I still feel like my hands are tied. Like I'm belted in somehow with limited choices. Limited possibilities."

Tiffany looked at me and raised an eyebrow.

"Eric," she said. "If we're all rugrats of the universe like Bill said, and if we're all standing here in line waiting to inherit big-time from the mind of the All, then wouldn't that mean, for *all* of us somewhere down the road, all things *are* possible?"

I looked at Tiffany as the gears in my head starting spinning faster.

No one spoke.

Jerry broke the silence.

"Lock and load."

# Sixty-four

"With that settled," said Tiffany with a warm smile, "if you gentlemen will excuse me, I gotta go be creative."

"Take care," said Mitchell.

The rest of us echoed the feeling.

Just before she stepped out onto the sidewalk, Tiffany turned around, looked me straight in the eye, and winked. Then she disappeared out the door. And part of me went with her.

*There's something about that girl...*

# Sixty-five

After Tiffany left, I thought more about what she had just said to me. Suddenly the gears meshed. All things *are* possible. Damn. Felt my brain leave the launch pad with that one.

Talk about deploying to a world of endless opportunities. But

Leaving The Launch Pad

how many lifetimes would it take to reach *that* point? In the meantime, how do we deal with *today*?

So as usual, I had another question.

"Ravi," I said, "it sure looks like good things are waiting for us in the future, but is there anything else we can sink our teeth into right now?"

"Sure. Reminders."

"What do you mean?"

"Take crisis for example. It's a great reminder. The stress of seeing the pain of others in a tight spot 'kicks us up a notch'. You could say our vibration increases, and we feel more in tune with things. As a result, we work together as one and help each other deal with the problem. And that feeling of oneness and caring is a preview of that better world that's waiting for us." He paused. "But after the crisis has passed…"

"We crawl back in our holes," I said.

"As I said, it's just a reminder."

Suddenly, I thought of that supercharged feeling I felt in combat.

# Sixty-six

"Hold on," I said. "If the stress of crisis raises our vibration, could the extreme stress of war create a *stronger* reminder of who we are? Could we, in some twisted sort of way, actually enjoy fighting and killing each other because we feel even *more* in tune with our true potential?"

"Interesting idea, isn't it?" said Ravi. "Your World War II correspondent Ernie Pyle felt it when he said, 'War makes strange giant creatures out of us little routine men who inhabit the earth.' He knew there was something bigger going on. And there was a First World War veteran who *really* got the idea. In his book, *Wisdom of the Overself*, Dr. Paul Brunton calls war 'an awakener' and that…"

"Who's Brunton?" said Bill.

"English soldier. Served in a tank division in the First World War. After the war, he split for the Himalayas. Same mountains I found myself in. Guess he was looking for a wise man or a guru to tell him what the hell *that* war was all about."

"After runnin' around in those sardine cans," said Bill, "I can see where *he* was comin' from."

Nods of agreement from around the tables.

"Anyway," said Ravi, "he said war was an 'an awakener' and that this world is but a contrivance to draw forth latent perfection."

"At ease," said Bill. "At ease. Contrivance? Latent perfection?"

"Yeah. A contrivance is a set-up. A plan laid down ahead of time. Kind of like a trap. Latent perfection is that compassionate and caring part of us that's still asleep. He says war is supposed to wake us up, get our full attention, and remind us there's a better way. And as far as getting our full attention, there's nothing quite like mortal combat."

"You got that right," I said.

"But do you see?" said Ravi, "Be it inner conflict with yourself, a fight between two people, or big-time troubles and war between countries, *conflicts are reminders*. The letters 're' mean, 'back to'. *Re*mind means *back to* the mind. Back to the Mind that allows us to experience all the ups and downs of life."

"Re-mind!" said Mitchell suddenly. "*Now* the pieces fit."

"What pieces?" I said.

Mitchell looked at me.

"The pieces I was trying to tell Shaggy about. How when it gets dark enough, the stars come out?"

"Oh yeah. I remember you saying something about that."

"Well," he said, "I've been thinkin'. We know memories of war can take us to some pretty dark places. That's a given. I just couldn't figure out how the stars fit in while we're muckin' around in that darkness. Then it sank in that if I look up at those stars, I'm lookin' at the very thing that can lead me *out* of that darkness. Light. *Star* light. And with billions and billions of stars out there, the universe has got to be *filled* with the stuff. Even if we can't see it all because our eyes aren't set up to do that, it's still there. So, I kept askin' myself, where did all that light come from? Then today Ravi talks about that famous command in the Bible, 'Let there *be* light.' And of course, *that's* where it all came from. A flip of the switch. All made to order on day one. And what do we meet when we go back to that light-filled startin' gate? The mind that set this whole crazy game of life in motion in the first place. *The* Mind. Re-mind."

"I sort of follow that," I said.

"Hey," said Mitchell. "It might not pass muster, but it works for me."

Ravi smiled.

Jerry had been kind of quiet, until now.

"Yup," he said. "Pretty crazy, alright."

I started to open my mouth again when Ravi smiled and said, "I know, Eric. You want to know *why* things are so crazy."

"I do."

"Because we get so tangled up in our own troubles we only see what's right in front of our face. Like being all tangled up in a spider web. We don't step back and look at the big picture. But I've got something here," he said with a knowing look in his eye, "that might help you step *way* back and get a whole new perspective."

# Sixty-seven

Reaching into his back pocket, Ravi pulled out a folded piece of paper and spread it out on the table. Two pictures stared up at the group.

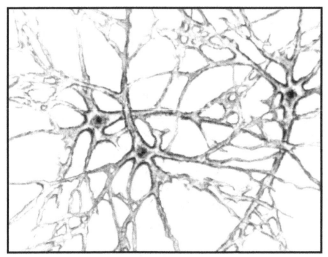

Drawing By The Author

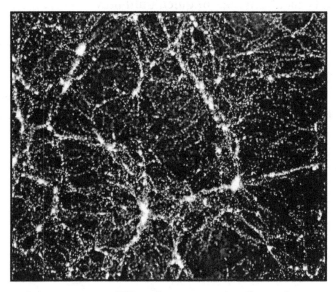

Image courtesy of Virgo Supercomputing Consortium

"Speakin' of spider webs," said Bill leaning over for a closer look, "What are those? Dusty ones?"

"No," said Ravi. "These are pictures of the vast cosmos inside our heads."

"What?" I said.

"This picture," he said putting his finger on the top one, "is a drawing of three brain cells. The other picture is a computer image showing how galaxies are laid out in space."

Jerry, Bill, Mitchell, and I looked down at the pictures. Then we looked up at Ravi, back down at the pictures, then back up to Ravi again.

"There's an age-old saying," said Ravi, "that goes, 'As above, so below. As below, so above. It means whatever happens big, is going to happen small, and the other way around. Galaxies," he said, "spin in space, hurricanes swirl in the atmosphere, tornadoes twist a tighter circle, and water circles the drain. Things like that. Our mind uses little brain cells inside our head, the *universal* mind uses bigger things inside *its* head."

Jerry, Bill, Mitchell, and I just kept looking at Ravi.

He smiled and said, "Almost done."

We kind of nodded.

"So just like the nerves in your fingertips," he said, "that run up your arm and connect to your brain, you and I are like the nerves in the 'fingertips' of the All that run up and connect to this universal message center. And that connection makes each and every one of us a foreign-affairs officer for the office of the All; its personal representative. That means all of us are 'joined at the hip', and one with," he spread his arms wide, "this really big mind." He paused. "Which, by the way, is what mystics have been telling us for thousands of years."

"Mystics?" I said.

"Those who believe union with the divine is *experienced* rather than just talked about."

"Oh."

# Sixty-eight

Bill had been thinking about all this with the same dreamy look in his eyes he got after he'd had a few. Then his thoughts shifted, and he came back down to earth.

"Sounds like we *are* all one. But does that mean if I kick someone in the ass, I'm kickin' myself?"

"That's right," said Ravi. "Whatever you put out there is what you get back. Whatever you give, is what you receive. Someone else's foot might be in that boot, but sooner or later, it'll come right back at ya."

I kind of smiled at the thought. But the smile faded fast. Threatening memories suddenly stirred in the darkness, and with the promise of pain, began to crawl from the shadows.

"But what about…?"

"Eric," said Ravi, "What you did in the past is *not* who you are today.

A brief flash of light sent those memories double-timing back to where they came from.

"But now what?" I said. "What do we do with all this info?"

"Wake up from the storm of forgetfulness we're lost in and find our way home. And in the process, help others do the same if they want help. Some don't. But just know there are signposts for each one of us, all along the way, marking our own unique path to that awakening."

"And how do we recognize these signposts?"

"Just pay close attention to your hunches and gut feelings. They'll guide you. Plus, they say the eyes are the windows to the soul. Well, the soul, like the rest of us, has got to have a direct connection to the All. Right?"

I nodded.

"So look into the eyes of the people you meet in your travels. Look into those windows and search for the source of all. Those eyes may be clouded by the struggles and pain in life, but the more of the All you see in others, the more of It you'll see in yourself." He paused. "And that," he added, "will lead you into the magical world of the mystical where Einstein said the most beautiful emotion we can feel comes from."

104

With those words, Ravi explained that it was time for him to hit the road again. Said he didn't really know where he was headed. Just went wherever the spirit led him.

Bill also said it was time to move on. Work was calling. And he had a happier wife waiting for him at home.

After warm farewells to both of them, Jerry, Mitchell, and I sat lost in thought.

More and more of my puzzle pieces were fitting together, but it still felt like there was something missing. A big something. Even so, I still felt like I was on that upward climb.

But once again, life would take care of that and bring me back down, hard. *Real* hard.

# Sixty-nine

The news of Tiffany's death floored me. She may have been high-class, but the mean streets had managed to reach up, grab her, and didn't let go.

The sudden nose-dive from the world of inspiring ideas back down to the 'real' world with Tiffany's murder was kind of like jumping off a moving train and not being able to get my legs going fast enough in time.

Fell flat on my face.

They caught Tiffany's killer, no problem. He never left the scene. The maid found him sitting on the edge of the bed, crying about how sorry he was.

Didn't help me, though. My demons said, "Let's party!"

And that, they did. Lost in a daze of grief and anger, I bounced off jagged emotional walls of pain all the way back to the well-oiled atmosphere of drunk-filled barrooms.

Once again, the bloody nails of mistress alcohol sank deep into my life. Deep enough this time to scrape the bone. By the end of three weeks, my apartment looked like it had been ground zero for a non-stop fraternity bash.

# Seventy

Three o'clock in the morning. A park bench on the Boston Common. Me and a raging hangover. Head pounding, stomach heaving, I struggled to sit up. Finally made it.

Sat with my head in my hands and once again, wondered if death might be an improvement over the way I felt right now.

I knew there was one way to find out...

Suddenly, the weight of a hand on my shoulder.

*Great,* I thought. *Now all I need is to be arrested.* I lifted my head and looked up into the hooded face of the Grim Reaper.

Above the timeless grin of the ever-patient soul collector, empty eye sockets. Windows to eternal darkness. Held in a boney fist, curved blade of an ancient scythe.

Graveyard vapors. Dust and mold.

I froze as the Reaper gazed deep into my soul. His words echoed down ageless corridors of death and hissed through lifeless teeth.

*"Want to find out if death is an improvement? I'm at your service."*

He cocked his head and leaned a little closer.

*"Hmmm?"*

Desperately groping for words, I leaned back a little farther.

"I...I..."

The Reaper bent even closer.

I leaned back even farther.

Fearing what might happen next, I shook my head angrily and said, "No!"

That was all it took. The vision disappeared in a heartbeat.

*Oh man! Enough of this shit!*

I stood up, and swaying slightly, headed to Park Street station to find a cab. Scary as hell, but at least I knew the vision hadn't been real. Thankful for that.

Plus, I was lucky I hadn't been mugged.

But I wasn't out of the woods yet.

Grim Reaper

# Seventy-one

When I finally got back to my place and saw the mess, I let out a low groan.

Crushed beer cans everywhere. Pizza boxes. Some empty. Some with half-eaten slices glued to the bottom by time and mold. The mold, like some alien life form just waiting to creep out and take over the world.

And the smell…

*Eric?* I thought. *Do you want to die, or do you want to puke?*

I made it to the toilet just in time.

When I was done, I sat on the floor. Weak. Trembling. Struggling for breath. Felt a chasm of despair slowly open beneath me.

*Now what?*

Hopelessness reached up from the depths with icy fingers. Piercing cold. Fighting for control, I felt myself being pulled downward.

*It's over*, I thought. *Screw the puzzle.*

Then, without really thinking about it, I just let go. I surrendered, and the light went on. The light *behind* the scenes.

*The missing piece:* my connection to all possibilities.

Then, almost before I knew it, I was on my feet staring directly into the searing brightness. My next thought also seemed to have a life of its own. A choice rooted deep in my soul.

I swore right then and there to quit drinking – permanently.

Finally, a solid step on my path to true healing.

Didn't know how many twists and turns the path would make, but at least I was at the entrance and ready to advance.

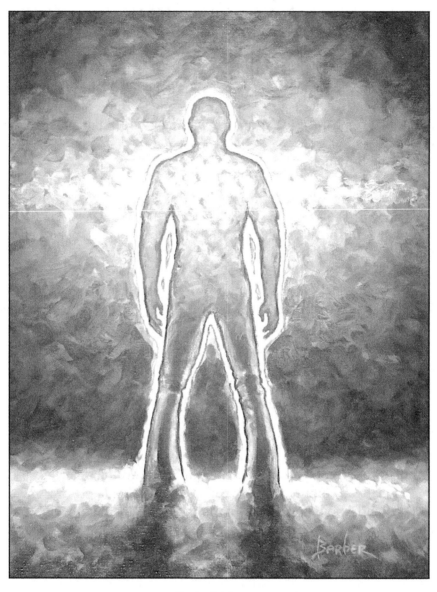

Searing Brightness

And then just as suddenly as the light went on, it was gone. But instead of a sense of loss, I was filed with a new sense of hope. From a place deep inside, a whole new feeling of freedom.

*Free at last,* I thought. *Out of restraints and free at last.*

Free At Last

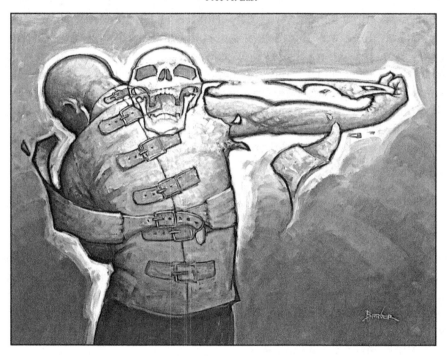

# Seventy-two

My flash of insight didn't last long, but it sure got its point across. Surrender to win. Just allow. Give up the struggle, give pain its freedom, and let the healing begin.

*Sounded* easy. But I knew facing my demons with soul-searing honesty *wouldn't* be. Plus, when Ravi was leaving he said flashes of insight aren't something you can just make happen. Big or small, they kind of pop up when they're ready. But it's cool when they do.

Then there was the idea of surrender and hard work at the same time. Kind of weird. Like they're opposite each other. But it still didn't sound as bad as slaying demons. And meditation would help smooth things out and tie it all together. Ravi said meditation requires discipline. The army taught me plenty of that.

I also knew the Vet Centers and the heavy-duty pros were waiting for me if I needed them. Plus, I'd have the support of Mitchell and the crew back at his place.

Why not?

I'll even pick up that pencil again and write. And of course, get back to painting.

And covering my back? *All* of the All.

Finally, a way out of the quicksand of darkness I stepped into when I got off a plane and my foot hit the ground of a distant, desert land. And as I traveled my path, I would now be able to turn and help others. I would now be able to share my experiences with any veteran seeking the light.

With *anyone* looking for it.

My pizza lovers would be happy too because I'd still be deliverin'.

And then, a vision of Tiffany. A vision with words I sensed, more than heard.

*Welcome back, Eric. I'll keep an eye out for ya.*

# Seventy-three

Mitchell, Jerry, and I were sitting at the desk outside Mitchell's place.

The evening was warm, and a glass of iced tea sat in front of each one of us. A couple of empty pizza boxes sat in the middle of the desk. It was one of those rare moments when there was no traffic, and we just sat there comfortably soaking up the quiet.

It had been a year since I first walked down this street trying to get myself killed. A lot had happened since then.

My sobriety was getting stronger, and we'd heard from Bill that he and his wife were enjoying *his* sobriety out in Ohio.

Mitchell had filled Shaggy in on his thoughts on darkness, stars, and a return to the Mind. Shaggy said that if the darkness hadn't brought him to the door of Mitchell's place with a gun to his head, he wouldn't be on the road to recovery right now. Said he'd be dead.

I still missed Tiffany, but acceptance was helping me with my feelings in that department.

Plus, we got occasional cards from Ravi. The last one told us he was somewhere in the Australian outback and how he thought of us when he was out in the desert at night. On it, he said, "Next time you look up into the night sky, think of each star as a window letting you look right into the heart of the All and ask yourself what you see. No stars? No problem. Grab a book with pictures of stars in it. That works, too."

Good ole Ravi. He was only here for an instant, but we miss him.

So as my mind swept back over the landscape of the past year, I looked at Mitchell and Jerry, and raised my glass. Without my having to say a word, they understood and raised their own glasses in a toast to that understanding.

The preceding story was fiction.
The following stories are true.

Several years ago, I, the author, met a real estate agent who had been in the Merchant Marines in World War II. His ship was torpedoed in the Pacific, and he and his buddy jumped overboard and swam to get away from the sinking ship before it sucked them down.

At one point the agent turned around and saw that the ship had started to roll and the smokestack was coming down on top of both of them. There was no way they could swim free in time.

Suddenly someone grabbed the agent by the back of the shirt collar and pulled him out of the way. The stack came down and killed his buddy. The agent immediately turned around to see who had saved him. There was nobody there.

# THE STORY BEHIND THE PAINTING

# Part I

Shortly after I slammed into the world of sobriety, the idea for the Vietnam painting slammed into me. The energy that came with it was so strong I stopped talking, my vision blurred, and the hair on my arms stood up. In that instant, I saw the completed painting in my mind.

But I didn't go near it for over a year; dark memories from my time as a Vietnam-era army medic. Then with the encouragement of a friend, I finally put it on canvas (1988).

Not having my own studio at the time, I painted it in several different locations. One of those places was in the attic of a friend's house. There was an old set of encyclopedias stored away up there that I liked to browse through when I wasn't painting. It was during that time I had a very special dream.

117

I dreamt I was sitting on the edge of my bed looking at a flower in a glass of water on the bedside table. I picked up the glass to look at the flower more closely, when a very distinct voice behind my left ear said, "Yeah, but it's dead."

It was then I realized the flower was starting to wilt. So, I put the glass back on the table and woke up.

I turned on the light (about 3 A.M.) and picked up a book lying on the bed beside me. I opened it at random and my eyes fell on the following lines.

## *VEDANTA for the Western World*

*"Each successive age needs a new and characteristic presentation of the truths of religion. For these presentations, once they have been spoken or written down, are like cut flowers: they slowly begin to shrivel, they become dry and dead. Men often treasure dead flowers, for the memory which clings to them, and this is very natural: but one must not forget they are dead. Those who cling too devotedly to the dead flowers, to the letter of the law, lose consciousness of its undying spirit."*

At the same time as this dream, one of the articles I came across in the old encyclopedia stated that love of fellow man is one of the highest goals man can aim for. It's also the spirit of the painting given to me.

\* \* \*

He was actively planning his own suicide when he saw the painting on a poster advertising the local Vet Center (readjustment counseling). When I met him, he was back from the brink and doing fine. He said the painting brought him in, and he got the help he needed.

118

# Part II

Plato said only the dead have seen the end of war. Great. So now what do we do?

Science speaks of energy. Religion speaks of spirit. They both agree we came from this ethereal world. But when we look around, we find ourselves in a free-fire zone of one harsh reality.

Stories vary as to why we forget where we came from. But universal teachings agree, when we're ready, we return. So, it's up to us as individuals to rise above the storm, head back, and help others along the way if they want help. Some don't.

Pressed for time? Not to worry. When the Buddha attained enlightenment, he remembered thousands of his previous lives.

And where do we rise to? Ancient wisdom speaks of higher planes of existence. Quantum physics talks of parallel universes. Christ said his Father's house has a whole bunch of rooms in it. Whatever is going on, it sounds like there's plenty of room for all of us.

Plus each one of has what it takes to get there. "...*all things* are *possible to him that believeth.*" (Mark 9:23). *All* things add up to be *a lot* of things.

Lock and load.

As far as that ethereal world we came from in the first place? It's a place many philosophies have referred to as 'home', and the inspiration for the Vietnam painting was just a reminder of that place.

And the voice behind my left ear? Just keeping the phones line open so the message gets through.

It did.


The painting (oil – 36"x48") is on permanent display at the Vet Center in White River Junction, Vermont.

**Locations and phone numbers of Vet Centers in the US and Puerto Rico.**

**For up to date information, Google: Vet Centers**

Alabama –
| | |
|---|---|
| Birmingham | 205-212-3122 |
| Huntsville | 256-539-5775 |
| Mobile | 251-478-5906 |
| Montgomery | 334-273-7796 |

Alaska –
| | |
|---|---|
| Anchorage | 907-563-6966 |
| Fairbanks | 907-456-4238 |
| Wasilla | 907-376-4318 |

American Samoa –            684-699-3760

Arizona –
| | |
|---|---|
| Lake Havasu City | 928-505-0394 |
| Mesa | 480-610-6727 |
| Phoenix | 602-640-2981 |
| Prescott | 928-778-3469 |
| Tucson | 520-882-0333 |
| Yuma | 928-271-8700 |

Arkansas –
| | |
|---|---|
| Fayetteville | 479-582-7152 |
| Little Rock | 501-324-6395 |

California –

| | |
|---|---|
| Bakersfield | 661-323-8387 |
| Bonita | 858-404-8380 |
| Chatsworth | 818-576-0201 |
| Chico | 530-899-6300 |
| Citrus Heights | 916-535-0420 |
| Concord | 925-680-4526 |
| Corona | 951-734-0525 |
| Commerce | 323-728-9966 |
| Eureka | 707-444-8271 |
| Fresno | 599-487-5660 |
| Gardena | 310-767-1221 |
| Garden Grove | 714-776-0161 |
| Mission Viejo | 949-348-6700 |
| Modesto | 209-569-0713 |
| Oakland | 510-763-3904 |
| Palmdale | 661-267-1026 |
| Peninsula | 650-299-0672 |
| Rohnert Park | 707-586-3295 |
| Sacramento | 916-566-7430 |
| San Bernardino | 909-801-5762 |
| San Diego | 858-642-1500 |
| San Francisco | 415-441-5051 |
| San Jose | 408-993-0729 |
| San Luis Obispo | 805-782-9101 |
| San Marcos | 855-898-6050 |
| Santa Cruz | 831-464-4575 |
| Temecula | 951-302-4849 |
| Ventura | 805-585-1860 |
| Victorville | 760-261-5925 |
| West Los Angeles | 310-641-0326 |

Colorado –

|  |  |
|---|---|
| Boulder | 303-440-7306 |
| Colorado Springs | 719-471-9992 |
| Denver | 303-326-0645 |
| Fort Collins | 970-221-5176 |
| Grand Junction | 970-245-4156 |
| Pueblo | 719-583-4058 |

Connecticut –

|  |  |
|---|---|
| Danbury | 203-790-4000 |
| Hartford | 860-563-8800 |
| New Haven | 203-932-9899 |
| Norwich | 860-887-1755 |

Delaware –

|  |  |
|---|---|
| Georgetown | 302-225-9110 |
| Wilmington | 302-994-1660 |

District of Columbia –

|  |  |
|---|---|
| Washington | 202-726-5212 |

Florida –

|  |  |
|---|---|
| Bay County | 850-522-6102 |
| Clearwater | 727-549-3600 |
| Clermont | 352-536-6701 |
| Daytona Beach | 386-366-6600 |
| Fort Lauderdale | 954-356-7962 |
| Ft. Myers | 239-652-1861 |
| Gainesville | 352-331-1408 |
| Jacksonville | 904-232-3621 |
| Jupiter | 561-422-1220 |
| Lakeland | 863-284-0841 |
| Melbourne | 321-254-3410 |
| Miami | 305-718-3712 |

| | |
|---|---|
| Naples | 239-403-2377 |
| New Port Richey | 727-697-5176 |
| Ocala | 352-317-2563 |
| Okaloosa | 850-651-1000 |
| Orlando | 407-857-2800 |
| Palm Beach | 561-422-1201 |
| Pensacola | 850-456-5886 |
| Pompano Beach | 954-984-1669 |
| Sarasota | 941-927-8285 |
| St. Petersburg | 727-549-3633 |
| Tallahassee | 850-942-8810 |
| Tampa | 813-228-2621 |

Georgia –
| | |
|---|---|
| Atlanta | 404-321-6111 |
| Augusta | 706-729-5762 |
| Columbus | 706-596-7170 |
| Lawrenceville | 404-728-4195 |
| Macon | 478-477-3813 |
| Marietta | 404-327-4954 |
| Savannah | 912-961-5800 |

Guam –
| | |
|---|---|
| Guam | 671-472-7160 |

Hawaii –
| | |
|---|---|
| Hilo | 808-969-3833 |
| Honolulu | 808-973-8387 |
| Kailua-Kona | 808-329-0574 |
| Kauai | 808-246-1163 |
| Maui | 808-242-8557 |
| Kapolei | 808-674-2414 |

Idaho –

| Boise | 208-342-3612 |
| Pocatello | 208-232-0316 |

Illinois –

| Aurora | 630-585-1853 |
| Chicago | 773-962-3740 |
| Chicago Heights | 708-754-8885 |
| East St. Louis | 618-397-6602 |
| Evanston | 847-332-1019 |
| Forest Park | 708-383-3225 |
| Moline | 309-762-6955 |
| Orland Park | 708-444-0561 |
| Peoria | 309-689-9780 |
| Rockford | 815-395-1276 |
| Springfield | 217-492-4955 |

Indiana –

| Crown Point | 219-736-5633 |
| Evansville | 812-473-5993 |
| Fort Wayne | 240-460-1456 |
| Indianapolis | 317-988-1600 |
| South Bend | 574-231-8480 |

Iowa –

| Cedar Rapids | 319-378-0016 |
| Des Moines | 515-284-4929 |
| Sioux City | 712-255-3808 |

Kansas –

| Manhattan | 785-587-8257 |
| Wichita | 316-265-0889 |

Kentucky –

| | |
|---|---|
| Lexington | 859-253-0717 |
| Louisville | 502-634-1916 |

Louisiana –
| | |
|---|---|
| Alexandria | 318-466-4327 |
| Baton Rouge | 225-761-3140 |
| New Orleans | 504-565-4977 |
| Shreveport | 318-861-1776 |

Maine –
| | |
|---|---|
| Bangor | 207-947-3391 |
| Caribou | 207-496-3900 |
| Lewiston | 207-783-0068 |
| Portland | 207-780-3584 |
| Springvale | 207-490-1513 |

Maryland –
| | |
|---|---|
| Annapolis | 410-605-7826 |
| Baltimore | 410-764-9400 |
| Clinton | 301-856-7173 |
| Dundalk | 410-282-6144 |
| Elkton | 410-392-4485 |
| Silver Spring | 301-589-1073 |

Massachusetts –
| | |
|---|---|
| Boston | 617-424-0665 |
| Brockton | 508-580-2730 |
| Hyannis | 508-778-0124 |
| Lowell | 978-453-1151 |
| New Bedford | 508-999-6920 |
| Springfield | 413-737-5167 |
| Worcester | 508-753-7902 |

Michigan –

| | |
|---|---|
| Clinton Township | 586-412-0107 |
| Dearborn | 313-277-1428 |
| Detroit | 313-576-1514 |
| Escanaba | 906-233-0244 |
| Grand Rapids | 616-285-5795 |
| Pontiac | 248-874-1015 |
| Saginaw | 989-321-4650 |
| Traverse City | 231-935-0051 |

Minnesota –
| | |
|---|---|
| Brooklyn Park | 763-503-2220 |
| Duluth | 218-722-8654 |
| New Brighton | 651-644-4022 |

Mississippi –
| | |
|---|---|
| Biloxi | 228-388-9938 |
| Jackson | 601-965-5727 |

Missouri –
| | |
|---|---|
| Colombia | 573-814-6206 |
| Kansas City | 816-753-1866 |
| Springfield | 417-881-4197 |
| St. Louis | 314-531-5355 |

Montana –
| | |
|---|---|
| Billings | 406-657-6071 |
| Great Falls | 406-452-9048 |
| Kalispell | 406-257-7308 |
| Missoula | 406-721-4918 |

Nebraska –
| | |
|---|---|
| Lincoln | 402-476-9736 |
| Omaha City | 402-346-6735 |

Nevada –
| | |
|---|---|
| Henderson | 702-791-9100 |
| Las Vegas | 702-251-7873 |
| Reno | 775-323-1294 |

New Hampshire –
| | |
|---|---|
| Gorham/Berlin | 603-752-2571 |
| Manchester | 603-668-7060 |

New Jersey –
| | |
|---|---|
| Bloomfield | 973-748-0980 |
| Lakewood | 908-607-6364 |
| Secaucus | 201-223-7787 |
| Trenton | 609-882-5744 |
| Ventnor | 609-487-8387 |

New Mexico –
| | |
|---|---|
| Albuquerque | 505-346-6562 |
| Farmington | 505-327-9684 |
| Las Cruces | 575-523-9826 |
| Santa Fe | 505-988-6562 |

New York –
| | |
|---|---|
| Albany | 518-626-5130 |
| Babylon | 631-661-3930 |
| Binghamton | 607-722-2393 |
| Bronx | 718-367-3500 |
| Brooklyn | 718-624-2765 |
| Buffalo | 716-862-7350 |
| Harlem | 212-426-2200 |
| Hicksville | 516-348-0088 |
| Manhattan | 212-742-9591 |
| Mieton | 845-342-9917 |
| Rochester | 585-232-5040 |

| Staten Island | 718-816-4499 |
| Syracuse | 315-478-7127 |
| Watertown | 315-782-5479 |
| White Plains | 914-682-6250 |
| Woodhaven | 718-296-2871 |

North Carolina –
| Charlotte | 704-549-8025 |
| Fayetteville | 910-488-6252 |
| Greensboro | 336-333-5366 |
| Greenville | 252-355-7920 |
| Jacksonville | 910-703-0699 |
| Raleigh | 919-856-4616 |

North Dakota –
| Bismarck | 701-224-9751 |
| Fargo | 701-237-0942 |
| Minot | 701-852-0177 |

Ohio –
| Canton | 330-454-3120 |
| Cincinnati | 513-763-3500 |
| Cleveland | 216-707-7901 |
| Columbus | 614-257-5550 |
| Dayton | 937-461-9150 |
| Parma | 440-845-5023 |
| Toledo | 419-213-7533 |

Oklahoma –
| Lawton | 580-585-5880 |
| Muskogee | 918-577-3699 |
| Oklahoma City | 405-456-5184 |

| | |
|---|---|
| Tulsa | 918-628-2760 |

Oregon –
| | |
|---|---|
| Bend | 541-749-2112 |
| Eugene | 541-465-6981 |
| Grants Pass | 541-479-6912 |
| Portland | 503-688-5361 |
| Salem | 503-362-9911 |

Pennsylvania –
| | |
|---|---|
| Bristol | 215-823-4590 |
| DuBois | 814-372-2095 |
| Erie | 814-453-7955 |
| Harrisburg | 717-782-3954 |
| Lancaster | 717-283-0735 |
| McKeesport | 412-678-7704 |
| Norristown | 215-823-5245 |
| Philadelphia | 215-924-4670 |
| Philadelphia | 215-627-0238 |
| Pittsburgh | 412-920-1765 |
| Scranton | 570-344-2676 |
| Williamsport | 570-327-5281 |

Puerto Rico –
| | |
|---|---|
| Arecibo | 787-879-4510 |
| Ponce | 787-841-3260 |
| Rio Piedras | 787-749-4409 |

Rhode Island –
| | |
|---|---|
| Providence | 401-739-0167 |

South Carolina –
| | |
|---|---|
| Charleston | 843-789-7000 |
| Columbia | 803-765-9944 |

|            |              |
|------------|--------------|
| Greenville | 864-271-2711 |
| Myrtle Beach | 843-232-2441 |

South Dakota –
| Rapid City | 605-348-0077 |
|------------|--------------|
| Sioux Falls | 605-330-4552 |

Tennessee –
| Chattanooga | 423-855-6570 |
|-------------|--------------|
| Johnson City | 423-928-8387 |
| Knoxville | 865-545-4680 |
| Memphis | 901-544-0173 |
| Nashville | 615-366-1220 |

Texas –
| Abilene | 352-232-7925 |
|---------|--------------|
| Amarillo | 806-354-9779 |
| Austin | 512-416-1314 |
| Beaumont | 409-347-0124 |
| Corpus Christi | 361-854-9961 |
| Dallas | 214-361-5896 |
| El Paso | 915-772-0013 |
| Fort Worth | 817-921-9095 |
| Harker Heights | 254-953-7100 |
| Houston | 713-587-4002 |
| Houston | 713-523-0884 |
| Houston | 713-682-2288 |
| Laredo | 956-723-4680 |
| Lubbock | 806-792-9782 |
| McAllen | 956-631-2147 |
| Mesquite | 927-288-8030 |
| Midland | 432-697-8222 |
| San Antonio | 210-688-0606 |
| San Antonio | 210-650-0422 |

| | |
|---|---|
| Pantego | 817-274-0981 |

Utah –
| | |
|---|---|
| Provo | 801-377-1117 |
| Saint George | 435-673-4494 |
| Salt Lake City | 801-584-1294 |

Vermont –
| | |
|---|---|
| South Burlington | 802-862-1806 |
| White River Junction | 802-295-2908 |

Virginia –
| | |
|---|---|
| Alexandria | 703-360-8633 |
| Norfolk | 757-623-7584 |
| Richmond | 804-353-8958 |
| Roanoke | 540-342-9726 |
| Virginia Beach | 757-248-3665 |

Washington –
| | |
|---|---|
| Bellingham | 360-733-9226 |
| Everett | 425-252-9701 |
| Federal Way | 253-838-3090 |
| Seattle | 206-553-2706 |
| Spokane | 509-444-8387 |
| Tacoma | 253-565-7038 |
| Walla Walla | 509-526-8387 |
| Yakima | 509-457-2736 |

West Virginia –
| | |
|---|---|
| Beckley | 304-252-8220 |
| Charleston | 304-343-3825 |
| Huntington | 304-523-8387 |
| Martinsburg | 304-263-6776 |

| | |
|---|---|
| Morgantown | 304-291-4303 |
| Princeton | 304-425-5653 |
| Wheeling | 304-232-0587 |

Wisconsin –
| | |
|---|---|
| Green Bay | 920-435-5650 |
| La Crosse | 608-782-4403 |
| Madison | 608-264-5342 |
| Milwaukee | 414-434-1311 |

Wyoming –
| | |
|---|---|
| Casper | 307-261-5355 |
| Cheyenne | 307-778-7370 |
| Fort Collins | 970-221-517 |

# About the Author

**Tom Barber** was a Vietnam-era army medic unable to imagine the trauma of combat. Trying to help those physically and emotionally crippled by the chaos of war brought to life feelings of survival guilt and helplessness that would haunt him for years. Alcohol killed that pain. Then alcohol addiction almost killed him.

After his discharge in 1971, he became an award-winning illustrator of science fiction and fantasy paperback book jackets . . . for a while. Then personal and business turmoil sent him fleeing to the mountains of Arizona. There he landed in the ghost town of Jerome where he eventually slammed headlong into the world of sobriety. *Big* change. The result is this story.

Some of the concepts and ideas in this book may be considered controversial or 'far out.' Nonetheless, they exist and have played a major role in his journey back from the brink.

With his lady, Terri, of 28 years, he now lives in New Hampshire where he continues to paint and write.

Made in United States
North Haven, CT
17 September 2023

41674360R00078